3

THE THREAT TO THE COSMIC ORDER:

Psychological, Social, and Health Implications of Richard Wagner's RING OF THE NIBELUNG

Mental Health Library Series

Monograph 4

edited by
George H. Pollock, M.D., Ph.D.

THE THREAT TO THE COSMIC ORDER:

Psychological, Social, and Health Implications of Richard Wagner's RING OF THE NIBELUNG

Edited by
Peter Ostwald, M.D.
Leonard S. Zegans, M.D.

INTERNATIONAL UNIVERSITIES PRESS, INC.
Madison   Connecticut

Library of Congress Cataloging-in-Publication Data

The threat to the cosmic order : psychological, social, and health
  implications of Richard Wagner's Ring of the Nibelung / edited by
  Peter Ostwald, Leonard S. Zegans.
       p.   cm. — (Mental health library series ; monograph 4)
    Includes bibliographical references and index.
    ISBN 0-8236-6528-3
    1. Wagner, Richard, 1813-1883. Ring des Nibelungen. 2. Opera-
-Psychological aspects. 3. Opera—Social aspects. 4. Opera—Health
aspects. I. Ostwald, Peter F. II. Zegans, Leonard S.
III. Series.
ML410.W15T57   1996
782.1—dc20   96-24652
                                                                   CIP
                                                                   MN

Manufactured in the United States of America

This book is dedicated to the memory of Dr. Peter Ostwald who passed away last year. He was an inspiring colleague, friend, and scholar. He made extraordinary contributions to a better understanding of the relationship between psychological processes and the arts. His wisdom and humor will be missed by all who knew him.

Contents

Contributors

Alessandra Comini, Ph.D. University Distinguished Professor of Art History, Southern Methodist University, Dallas, Texas

Laurie Feldman Stage Director *Das Rheingold* and *Götterdämmerung* in 1990 San Francisco Opera *Ring* cycles

Herta Glaz Mezzo soprano; Adjunct Professor of Voice, University of California, Los Angeles; formerly sang with the Metropolitan Opera, San Francisco Opera, and other companies

Thomas S. Grey, Ph.D. Assistant Professor of Music, Braun Music Center, Stanford University, Stanford, California

Robert W. Gutman Former Dean of Graduate Studies, State University of New York

Hans Hotter Bass baritone, teacher and noted interpreter of Wotan and other roles at the Bayreuth Festspielhaus, Metropolitan Opera, San Francisco Opera, and many other international companies

David Clay Large, Ph.D. Professor of History, Montana State University, Bozeman, Montana

David Littlejohn Writer, critic, Professor of Journalism, University of California, Berkeley

Janis Martin Soprano, performed two Brünhildes in 1990 San Francisco Opera *Ring* cycles; performs with major opera companies in the United States and Europe

Franz Mazura Bass, performed Alberich in 1990 San Francisco Opera *Ring* cycles; performs with major opera companies in the United States and Europe

Peter Ostwald, M.D. Professor of Psychiatry and Medical Director of the Health Program for Performing Artists, University of California, San Francisco

Eric A. Plaut, M.D. Professor Emeritus, Department of Psychiatry and Behavioral Sciences, Northwestern University Medical School, Chicago, Illinois

George H. Pollock, M.D., Ph.D. Ruth and Evelyn Dunbar Distinguished Professor of Psychiatry and Behavioral Sciences Emeritus, Northwestern University Medical School, Chicago, Illinois; President, Chicago Institute of Psychoanalysis and the Center for Psychosocial Studies of Chicago

Fritz C. Redlich, M.D. Professor of Psychiatry Emeritus, Yale University School of Medicine, New Haven, and Department of Psychiatry and Behavioral Science, University of California, Los Angeles

Günter B. Risse, M.D., Ph.D. Professor and Chairman, Department of History of Health Sciences, University of California, San Francisco

Donald Runnicles Conductor of two 1990 San Francisco Opera *Ring* cycles; Music Director, San Francisco Opera

Steven Sokolow, M.A. President, Wagner Society of Northern California

Leonard S. Zegans, M.D. Professor of Psychiatry and Director of Education, Langley Porter Psychiatric Institute, University of California, San Francisco

Introduction

Peter Ostwald, M.D.

Richard Wagner's *Ring of the Nibelung* is one of the most impressive accomplishments ever created by the human mind, comparable in its artistic vision to Michelangelo's Sistine Chapel, in its historical proportions to Shakespeare's plays, and in its musical originality to Beethoven's string quartets. Each new production of Wagner's *Ring* places a tremendous responsibility on singers, musicians, directors, designers, and audiences. Our goal in this volume is to explore the psychological, social, and health implications of these music dramas and of the man who created them.

You will have noticed that this Symposium was organized by members of the University of California's Department of Psychiatry and the Health Program for Performing Artists. Our mission is to help the sick, to teach and practice good medicine, and to encourage interdisciplinary research, knowing that the connections between art and science go far back in recorded history.

While preparing for this Symposium, we were often asked what were the medical implications of the *Ring* that would justify holding such an event on a Health Sciences campus. The answer has been "Of course there are many." We can begin with the prolonged water-immersion of the Rhinemaidens; the gigantism and dwarfism of various *Ring* characters; Wotan's loss of an eye; Sieglinde's death in a bungled childbirth; the ambulance service run by the Valkyries for their maimed heroes; Brünnhilde's protracted sleep and exposure to fire on a rock; all kinds of wounds produced by spears and swords; psychedelic drugs put into magic potions, and much more.

But of course that is just the beginning. The *Ring* proceeds on many levels of symbolism and meaning to address a variety of psychological and social problems: incest, superstition, the renunciation of love, the psychodynamics of family life, the manifestations of greed and lust for power. As the late German musicologist Carl Dahlhaus (1971) pointed out, Wagner's *Ring of the Nibelung* "is about nothing less than the downfall of a world of law and force, and the dawn of an utopian age" (p. 81).

We hope readers will enjoy these discussions and be enlightened by their presenters' ideas. We have invited a truly remarkable group of historians, artists, musicologists, medical doctors, and other experts to address issues posed by the *Ring*. Readers will be exposed to a wide range of opinions and undoubtedly there will be controversy, as there usually is when Wagner's work is discussed. He was one of the most controversial figures of the nineteenth century: a genius, a revolutionary, and a bigot. He remains controversial today because certain of the ideas he espoused—the superiority of German art, the ascendancy of a master race, and the need to eradicate Jewish influence—were prophetic of the catastrophic events which have blighted the twentieth century. This book addresses certain of these issues along with the more pleasant and magical themes of the *Ring*.

Be prepared for a kaleidoscopic experience, a "Gesamtkunstwerk" to use Wagner's own neologism. And also be prepared for some overlap and repetition, another inevitable by-product of Wagnerism. He addresses us on so many different and conflicting levels that one is often left gasping, and sometimes exhausted.

The book begins with four keynote addresses, to introduce the Leifmotifs of Wagner's life, personality, and cosmology. It then elaborates on these by entering the fields which make his work so exciting: the *Ring* in the Mind, and the *Ring* in Performance. Some discussions are longer than others, not because their topics are more important but because some authors have devoted a lifetime of study to a very large area, while others were asked to focus their expertise on a limited or specific aspect. We thank all of them for their contributions.

REFERENCE

Dahlhaus, C. (1971), *Richard Wagner's Music Dramas*, tr. M. Whitall. London: Cambridge University Press.

1

Richard Wagner's Cosmology: Self-Deception, Self-Realization, and the Destruction of Nature

Leonard S. Zegans, M.D.

Audiences arrive at a performance of *The Ring* with a special sense of anticipation. Most attend not only to hear some gripping dramatic scenes or to pass judgment over a new, heralded tenor, but to place themselves under the spell of a brilliant story-teller and musical enchanter. The child in us is still enthralled by the idea of dragons, giants, and helmeted women carrying the bodies of heroes slung across their horses. Yet as adults we discover that there is a drama taking place not only upon the stage but within our own minds. Wagner is a shaman who evokes in us images usually sheltered from our awareness, but released by his fusion of music and drama. We are the ultimate instrument of Wagner's talent. He conjures from within us memories and images from our own unconscious hopes, fears, and emotions; he stretches our imagination, sending us from the present, to the archaic past, to glimpses of a prophetic future. We may judge his political views as wildly impractical, detest his anti-Semitic writings, recoil at his betrayal of his benefactors and wives, and yet continue to fall under his evocative spell.

There is of course something very dated about Wagner's nineteenth century Romantic images. His once innovative and provocative notions of music drama today seem wilted and rather grandiose. And yet all the contributors to this volume have found insights in *The Ring* which seem prophetically relevant to our current moment in history. He holds

1

a mirror up to our era's vanity, heroic striving, moral blindness, and lust for power.

The *Ring* cycle was his jeremiad, linking the fate of the earth to the impact of man's self-delusions, egoistic striving, and manipulations of nature. Through the complex figure of Wotan he reveals to us our own wish to dominate events and our frequent helplessness to prevent foretold disasters. The chief of the gods enacts the need to manipulate others through the exercise of power, while seeking to protect his own spontaneity and freedom. Over and against these themes, there is the constant presence of *nature*, powerful, mysterious, and yet fragile, reactive to the actions and desires of the gods, dwarfs, and men. When the cycle begins we are back at a point in mythic history when giants walked the earth, and gods descended from their heavens and communicated with humans. In this epoch the world had not yet been flattened by human rationality, subjecting the natural to its domination, and destroying the realm of the spirit. Yet at the beginning of the dramas all is not well. The gods seek to retreat from nature by withdrawing into the fortress of Valhalla and the Rhinemaidens mock and belittle the dwarf Alberich, provoking through their spiteful lack of empathy with another living creature, the rape of their gold.

Wagner is making a distinction between the sin against the self and the sin against the larger social and natural order. Thus Alberich desires the love or at least the lust of women, but comes to renounce the possibility of love in order to possess the Rhinegold and with it the ring and its power over others. His crime derives from frustration and he is willing to sacrifice a part of his nature in order to obtain power. Wotan, on the other hand, is willing to betray friends, his wife, and break oaths in order to achieve power for its own sake. He does not act out of frustration, but from a desire to acquire more freedom, mobility, and the possibility of endless change. Wotan threatens the cosmic order because of a demand which comes without provocation: the desire to expand limitlessly the domination of his ego. With Alberich there is a balance: he gains power but loses love. He understands that one acquisition is paid for by the loss of other possibilities. This same sense of balance does not restrain Wotan who believes that his acquisitions, such as Valhalla, can be bought without a price. He deceives and betrays the giants. His flaw is the conceit that others must pay for what he acquires and that no law of restraint or retribution should ever apply to him. He wishes for absolute freedom, the relief from any pain or cost which results from his actions. Yet there is always a reckoning for acquisitions, which Wotan later learns, when he must give up his eye in exchange for wisdom.

Understanding Wotan's insecurities is the key to the meaning of the entire cycle. He instructs the giants to build Valhalla before Alberich steals the ring. Who are his enemies? His anxiety arises from being situated in a cosmic environment whose origin, secrets, and future even he, as the most powerful of gods, does not comprehend. Thus Wagner touches upon a most fundamental human anxiety: our uncertainty about the basic nature of the cosmos in which we live. It is both the most familiar thing that we know and yet it is ultimately mysterious and alien. It possesses purposes, cycles, and laws which are completely beyond our comprehension. Man's earliest forays into religion and science were attempts to bring order and predictability into our understanding of the cosmos, so that human belief and action could be aligned with the laws of the universe. Yet the building of Valhalla is an evasion of the rule of "the natural order" and its replacement by personal control. Thus the giving up of Freia's golden apples represents a symbolic sacrifice of a natural gift in exchange for a fortress from which the gods could impose their own order upon nature. The dominating theme throughout *The Ring* is of the tension between man's will and the natural order. From the very beginning of the cycle the gods are in a state of uncertainty about their safety. They trust neither nature nor their own intuition and ability to keep them safe. That which they do not understand they fear. Valhalla represents all those attempts by man to avoid and evade nature and build a redoubt in which to feel secure. But this very alienation from nature threatens the cosmic order with ultimate destruction.

For Wagner and his generation, the terrifying realization arose that the world that they lived in might be destroyed not by some unforeseen natural disaster, or the rage of a jealous God, but through the greed and moral blindness of humankind. In the *Ring*, Wagner introduces us both to his own personal conflicts and the motifs which were shared with the Romantic revolutionaries of his generation. In the first half of the nineteenth century many poets, artists, philosophers, and musicians were concerned about the impact which the rationalism of the Enlightenment and the growth of industrial technology was having on the spiritual, emotional, and physical health of humanity. They were also appalled by the effects of rapid industrialization on the natural environment. The Romantics felt alienated from the ordered world that the Enlightenment had ushered into Europe. They endorsed the idea of the "free, spontaneous, creative impulse in man that knows no rules, or creates as the wind blows. . . . " They distrusted narrowness and specialization that "cribs and confines men and prevents the richest realization of the 'complete man,' which is conceived as a harmonious process, prevented hitherto only by human error or vice and the destructive institutions that this had bred" (Berlin, 1993, p. 69).

A common theme of the Romantics was a return to nature. For some this meant developing a simpler way of life in contrast to the rush, competitiveness, and complexities of civilized bourgeois society. To others it represented a yearning for a more primitive age when man expressed without conflict his basic instincts and generative passions. Poets such as Wordsworth had little sympathy with the materialists and scientists with their meddling and dissecting intellects. For him as for Wagner, nature was "an active principle," "a grandeur in the beating of the heart," a "primal sympathy" (Nicolson, 1961). We see this expressed many times in the *Ring* but perhaps with special poignancy in *Die Walküre* when the lovers open their hearts to each other and to the Spring. The cosmic symbol of spring is seen as endorsing their love vow which blazes in the breast of Sigmund, in contrast to Wotan's legalistic contracts written on the shaft of his spear.

Beyond the theme of nature there was also concern with individualism. The Romantics abhorred the eighteenth century philosophers' obsession with symmetry; the static rule of order, of established conventions, and with the narrow principles of conduct expected of middle-class society. We can hear these perspectives in debate in the great if somewhat tedious scenes between Fricka and Wotan: obligation versus spontaneity of desire. Yet Romanticism was also a child of unreason. Its emotionalism in politics has proven at times to be a dangerous potion: the cult of sensibility based on individual experience led many to become self-centered and disordered. Wagner could appreciate the liberation from a sense of constricting sin that Romanticism provided through its conviction that a resolute individual could mold his own destiny. Yet he was also aware that when feeling overwhelmed thought it could lead to physical and emotional excess. Such excesses must be balanced by reason, reflection, and most of all loving empathy. The twentieth century was to witness a wedding of romantic emotionalism and amoral scientific power to create the horror of German National Socialism which ironically idolized Wagner as a spiritual ancestor.

From the perspective of the nineteenth century Wagner could reflect back to a movement which began in the West with the Renaissance, a movement of such overwhelming force that within a few centuries it would radically disrupt the spiritual and intellectual beliefs which had dominated European thought and practice since the Middle Ages. Man's striving was no longer directed at understanding and accommodating to universal laws as described in myths and in the Scriptures, but was focused on dominating and mastering the workings of nature both for curiosity as well as for acquisitive ends. It was a question of grasping and transcending the uttermost possibilities. The laws and harmony of nature which were embodied in Erda, and the rules of domestic society which were Fricka's domain, were too restrictive for Wotan. Yet ironically his power itself came from these laws and the contracts that were inscribed on his spear. The guardian of treaties was impatient with the agreements that they enforced. He embodied the new spirit of post-Renaissance Europe, ever striving for mastery over nature without constraint and for novelty and change without regard to their social consequences.

By the mid-nineteenth century, the new industrial civilization no longer represented a familiar world adapted to human measure. Its ruthless competitiveness and massive concentration of labor and economic forces created a new environment which threatened human security and capacity for understanding. It made ever increasing demands on human adaptability. Man at the dawn of the Industrial Revolution was faced with the problem of escaping from his own ingenuity. As Loren Eiseley has said (quoting Pascal): "There is nothing which we cannot make natural and there is nothing natural which we cannot destroy" (Eiseley, 1960).

The Romantic artist in Wagner knew that we cannot equate technological and industrial progress with ethical and spiritual advances for humanity. The philosophers, artists, and writers of that time tried to imagine a superman, a hero who could be both a part of nature and yet surpass it. Yet the Alberichs, Wotans, and Siegfrieds did not understand that the true magic of the gold lay in its being embedded in nature. Through their greed for power or their ignorance, nature was robbed of her secrets and her magic exploited for selfish ends. When Wotan declares that he has no intention of ever returning the ring to the Rhinemaidens, he begins his decline; when Siegfried also refuses to return it, he seals his death. Erda warns of the dangers of this refusal, and in *Götterdämmerung* the very Ash Tree of Life on which the Norns spin their prophesies is destroyed at Wotan's order. Wotan thus represents the new order of man who can only become aware of his unique quality of being, his personal creative powers, by radically distancing himself from nature and defining himself through this difference (Rosinski, 1965).

With the tools for the transformation available to restless, power-seeking men, Wagner understood the terrible possibilities that lay inherent in an untrammeled technological revolution and devaluation of binding traditions. He foresaw the ravaging dangers to our planet which we now acknowledge each year on Earth Day. When nature becomes exploited and totally demythologized then the disasters that took place at the Chernobyl and Three-Mile Island nuclear power plants, acid rain, the destruction caused by the *Exxon Valdez* oil spill, and destruction of the rain forest become possible. Nature is life's home, but also a fragile, endangered dwelling place. The history of our species from its earliest records reveals a wish to transform nature's energies to meet mankind's need for control and independence.

We are thus confronted by three of the fundamental and inescapable conditions of man's struggle for liberation which are explored in the *Ring* cycle. First, man's creations almost immediately begin to escape from his control and assume an independent existence. Second, these creations invariably lead to consequences that were neither foreseen nor intended. Lastly, the consequences often turn out to be highly inconvenient and require a great deal of effort if they are to be undone (Rosinski, 1965).

What Wotan ultimately realizes is that by every advantage he establishes by means of deceit, he limits his own freedom of action. Creation based on betrayal and exploitation results not in self-liberation, but in self-limitation. As humanity tries to free itself from the multiple bonds of nature, it sets up new forces whose effect is to threaten this newfound freedom and create an even more fateful bondage.

It is recognition of this inevitability that pervades the most poignant scene between Wotan and Brünnhilde when he tells her that she must not carry out her wish that Sigmund slay Hunding, but instead that his beloved son must die. Wotan reveals to his daughter that he, the greatest of gods, through his deceitful contortions in seeking to regain the ring, has only created new complications which bind him even tighter to the laws and covenants from which he hoped to escape.

As a supreme artist, Wagner did not aspire to avoid the conflicts and contradictions that he observed in his own life and the world about him. He realized that humanity's salvation or destruction lay in working out the contradictions inherent in its drives and emotions. He saw that man was capable of both loyalty and betrayal, love and exploitation, keen memory and convenient forgetting. Through the discipline and inspiration of art these forces could be balanced and reconciled. Without structure, empathy, and love, man's drive for power would lead to demonic behavior. Twentieth century artists have understood that the center of civilized behavior does not always hold and that dissonance, fragmentation, and despair follow from its weakness. I believe that ultimately Wagner would have recoiled from the Nazi movement because he would have seen in it the triumph of the world-destructive will of Hagen, son of Alberich.

It is in the orchestra that all these conflicting forces and elements emerge and intertwine. Conscious and unconscious, past and present, hope and despair all arise from the sounds of the orchestra, like waves in our psyche exposing our own hidden desires and fears. The deepest nerve the music touches is that of a future apocalypse, brought about not through some stray crashing meteor or raging sunspot, but from the gradual accumulation of our own moral flaws.

In the end, Wagner the master egoist makes Brünnhilde the hero of the drama circle. It is through her capacity for empathy, loyalty, love, and self-sacrifice in the wake of her own strong impulses, that the hope of a new beginning arises. She embodies the seed of redemption that Wagner first had sought in the figure of Siegfried, but could not ultimately realize. He did not have the capacity to maintain a strong, unique self, and reach beyond that self to experience and express unselfish pathos for another. It is Brünnhilde who understands that if she is not able to act for herself, then none will act for her, and she also understands that if she is only to act for herself, she will lose herself.

In the *Ring* Wagner tells us that something must be kept sacred in the world, there must be values which individuals place above the demands of lust and power, if the very basis of creation is not to be endangered. This is a theme which was much more explicitly developed later in *Parsifal.*

One such value to be maintained is the integrity of self which is exemplified by Brünnhilde's death. Death for Wagner is part of the natural cycle. All creatures must die, even the gods. There is not tragedy in death, only in a life that does not live out its full potential and fearlessly pursue its destiny while also striving to achieve love and compassion.

These of course are very critical themes in the painful waning days of this century. As a physician I have seen medicine struggling to reconcile its wish to heal and comfort with a desire for new tools and knowledge. As physicians we strive to pursue the creative cutting edge of science and garner the power of new ideas and technologies. There is an intoxication in using the "ring" of science to transform organisms, create new diagnostic tools, and enable us to have privileged glimpses into the secrets of nature.

Today medicine struggles to balance the wishes of a Wotan for new power, with the insight of Brünnhilde that there is a greater strength still in the personal empathic responsiveness to the needs and concerns of another. Just as medicine rewards those who push back the frontiers of molecular biology and find more economical modes of delivering service, so too must it respect and acknowledge those who work for a more humane and equitably healthy society. If we treat our fellow humans and our environment only as instruments for personal domination then we become like Wotan, disillusioned and able to see the world with only one eye. Perhaps experiencing this supreme work of the last century will inspire us to build our own Rainbow Bridge, not to the fortress ghetto of Valhalla, but to a new creative union of self, humanity, and the earth itself. For as events in recent years have shown us, our survival depends upon transcending the narrow bounds of ego, ethnicity, or race, to embrace a broader vision of our common bonds of belonging. Plato said it well, in words that could have been addressed to Wotan, concerning the union between the individual, the community, and the universe:

> The ruler of the universe has ordered all things with a view to the excellence and preservation of the whole, and each part, as far as may be, has an action and passion appropriate to it. . . . One of these portions of the universe is thine own, unhappy man, which, however little, contributes to the whole; and you do not seem to be aware that this and every other creation is for the sake of the

whole in order that the life of the whole may be blessed; and that you are created for the sake of the whole, and not the whole created for the sake of you [Plato, p. 645].

REFERENCES

Berlin, I. (1993), The magus of the north. *NY Rev. Books,* 21/17:64–71.

Eiseley, L. (1960), Nature and miracle. *Horizon,* 2/6:25–32.

Nicolson, H. (1961), The romantic revolt. *Horizon,* 3/5:59–61.

Plato. Laws. In: *The Dialogues of Plato,* Vol. 2, tr. B. Jowett. New York: Random House, 1937.

Rosinski, H. (1965), *Power and Destiny.* New York: Frederick A. Prager.

2

A Passion to Command and Demand

Robert W. Gutman

This composer epitomized a complication not uncommon to young German artists: a recurring dissatisfaction with his German homeland; a decrying of what he felt to be the crudity of things German; and an aversion to his origins. This alienation was frequently expressed by German artists of the time by enthusiastically appropriating foreign, in particular French, models. Of course, at calmer moments this volatile young composer realized that his German heritage was the elemental medium through which his genius functioned; in fact, he never tired of crediting himself with the stoic virtues associated with the nation. But often despair over the German composer's plight, mainly the public's preference for foreign works, overwhelmed him. Ironically, like many others, he eventually sought a solution by settling in Paris. There he planned to defeat the enemy by playing its game, but playing it better. Paris, he well knew, remained *the* cultural arena of Europe, *the* tiltyard in which to win one's spurs as an artist. "From Paris," his mentor had insisted, "the fame and name of a man travel through the whole world" (Mozart, *Briefe*, Vol. 2, p. 277). "If Germany, my beloved fatherland, of which . . . I am proud, does not want to hold on to me," the young man trumpeted, "then in God's name, to the disgrace of the German nation, once again let France . . . become richer by another able German. In nearly all the arts . . . it is the Germans who have always excelled. But where have they found fortune and reputation? Certainly not in Germany!" (*Briefe*, Vol. 3, p. 220).

When considering this quandary, it may be helpful to remember that the young Goethe, too, had uncertainties about his German heritage, even for a while wondering whether German was a viable language for great poetry.

German composers, among them our hero, streamed toward Paris, and many proceeded to weave themselves into the very fabric of its musical life. The French beheld an astonishing development: the ascendancy and authority of German performers and composers in the city's concert rooms and theaters, to which they were bringing a new element, an international German musical art, conciliation, absorption, and the confronting of antitheses and their resolution being its characteristics. The Germans showed a particular gift for creating a stronger metal through an amalgam; like Goethe, our composer became an ultimate exemplar of the German tendency toward commingling—an eclectic extraordinaire.

The French recognized that musical hegemony was passing to the Germans but hedged acceptance of the fact with prideful conditions: that Paris remain the fork to which all European musicians tuned; in short, that it maintain its fame as the city that alone defined an international career. And, indeed, any German who wanted to think of himself in such terms—Stamitz, for example, among the Mannheimers, and Gluck from the court of the German Empress herself—rushed to the Seine to show his wares (just as artists and performers of the present day travel to the banks of the Hudson to get that New York review). Paris demanded a particularly high price for its artistic hospitality, linking success in the capital with the artists' readiness ever to sing hymns to French intellectual superiority. This presumption our hero was totally unwilling to entertain. Honesty, stubbornness, naiveté, or even patriotism, call it what you will, made it impossible for him hypocritically to mouth such things or so to sell himself as did Gluck, who excelled in this kind of guileful exercise. To the contrary, our musician loved to dwell upon what he felt to be the indigenous limitations to Parisian intellect, and the longer he remained in Paris the more obsessive these anti-French predilections waxed. He came to regard the French as pretentious and snobbish. How he bristled to hear himself referred to as a "dumb German" (*Briefe*, Vol. 2, p. 426); and, in turn, he defined French musicians as "cattle and beasts" (*Briefe*, Vol. 2, p. 346). He loathed their capital and especially its Opéra. The one infallible way to beguile the

French—lavishly to praise the beauty of their tongue—he defiantly excluded; in fact, he lost few opportunities to deride a language he declared to be an invention of the devil. (He spoke it very badly.)

Yet, he remained and struggled on in Paris, longing to do what Gluck had once done—to create imposing operas that would astound those he looked upon as the enemy, a goal he came to contemplate as a national mission "to teach the French more and more to know, esteem, and fear the Germans" (*Briefe*, Vol. 2, p. 427). He grew to look upon his work in Paris in terms of "doing honor to . . . the whole German nation" (*Briefe*, Vol. 2, p. 346) and as an experience that restored his belief in German values and heightened his sense of their superiority. Even when, occasionally, he gained the Parisians' applause, he railed at them: "The French are and always will be asses." He was not one to equivocate.

It particularly irritated him that in Germany companies giving foreign opera were sustained by singers who, despite their stage names, were really German. He looked upon the popularity of French operas on German stages as the creation of opera directors lacking in patriotism: "Were there but one patriot with authority, things would show a different complexion. . . . Of course, it would be an everlasting stain on Germany were we Germans seriously to begin to think as Germans, to act as Germans, to speak German, and even to sing in German!" (*Briefe*, Vol. 3, p. 393).

I might continue on about this composer's love of an extravagant wardrobe, observe that he came from a city whose accent other Germans particularly despised, comment on his penchant for cultivating friendships with individual Jews, and, above all, stress his place among the greatest composers to have written for the stage; but my little game would, in any case, soon have to end; the resemblances I might conjure would have run out; of course, the man I have been discussing and quoting was not Richard Wagner but one Wolfgang A. Mozart.

Mozart's and Wagner's Germanism and related Francophobia grew from the same roots. Leopold Mozart lectured his son on the atrocities committed by Louis XIV's troops when, in a campaign to seize the right bank of the Rhine, Louvois commanded them to lay waste the Palatinate: they mercilessly devastated Heidelberg, Mannheim, Speyer, Oppenheim, and Worms. The ruins were still to be seen at the time of the Mozarts' grand tour, and they inspected and pondered them. Leopold could also tell more personal tales: those of the alarms and fears in

Salzburg during his courtship of Wolfgang's mother, as the armies of Louis XV burned their way across Germany in a bold attempt to seize Vienna itself; indeed, they might well have succeeded had they not paused to plunder Prague.

The resentment helpless Germans felt against French expeditions that at will swept across a fragmented Reich was to find some redress in the figure of young Frederick of Prussia, who gradually made his case that the reassertion of German identity and the historic authority of the Reich lay not with the sluggish Habsburgs of Vienna trailing their ancient Imperial prerogatives but with the upstart, the vital Hohenzollern of Berlin.

Frederick set the pulse of German nationalism beating; in all the states of Germany he started to arouse a common, if often begrudging, admiration, which can be seen even in the letters of the Mozart family. Mozart would turn his gaze from a culturally atrophying Vienna toward Frederick's Berlin. Wagner was to trace much the same pattern. Both composers recurrently looked upon Vienna as the capital that might answer their aspirations. But by the end of his career, Mozart had begun a serious flirtation with Berlin; for his part, Wagner, ever attentive to the realities of power, fell into the arms of the Prussians as their avenging armies moved toward Paris—he wrote to Bismarck demanding that it be razed to the ground—and the Hohenzollern became the shadowy eminence under whose authority Bayreuth was permitted to develop: Ludwig of Bavaria, a paper king, could do nothing unless Bismarck nodded assent.

Had Mozart lived, he would have been 57 at the time of Richard Wagner's birth in Leipzig (May 22, 1813), an event concurrent with yet another French invasion of Germany, this one by Napoleon Bonaparte. But months earlier his Grande Armée had dissolved in the course of his famous retreat from Moscow, in reality a chaotic flight westward, the self-styled and self-crowned emperor doubling back over his route across Germany and the Rhine. Returned to the Tuileries and desperate to reassert his dominance, he had lost no time beginning the levy of fresh troops for yet another German expedition. In the time of the Bourbons, Vienna had been the center of German power and the coveted prize; now Berlin had become the goal. Wagner came into the world one day after Napoleon's pyrrhic victory at Bautzen and less than one hundred miles from this field of battle, which had claimed some 35,000 dead and wounded.

Napoleon's outrages upon German soil were but extensions, if usually more efficiently realized, of Bourbon prototypes. But by autumn the old French game had played itself out. The "Battle of Nations" unfolded before the infant Wagner's native city. The Germans and their Russian allies sent the French reeling from the gates of Leipzig, retiring toward Mainz, and then fleeing back to their very citadel, Paris itself. Within half a year it would fall and with it the French fantasy of a new Rome on the Seine.

Like Mozart, Wagner grew up with ruins to contemplate; and for both young Germans memories of childhood included tales of France's repeated rape of Germany. For those with a limited knowledge of European history and with only the Second and the Third Reich as vague points of reference, this reversal of the more familiar picture inevitably astonishes. But the recurrent and arrogant incursions of the French must be borne in mind if we are to understand why and how deeply Mozart resented them and why and how deeply Wagner detested them. (He, in fact, attempted to prohibit the speaking of French in Haus Wahnfried, his home in Bayreuth.) For Mozart the matter did not become obsession; for Wagner it did and could bring out his worst and—at times—his best. Let us turn to an example, revealing the composer at his most edifying.

The highly nationalistic *Lohengrin*, completed in the summer of 1848, became, in fact, the major point of transition in Wagner's political, intellectual, and artistic development. The opera emerged as a hymn of devotion to the Holy Roman Empire, the first or "Thousand Year" Reich that, astonishingly, did endure a millennium and even longer in spirit. The Habsburgs dissolved this—Karl der Grosse's—Reich less than a decade before Wagner's birth. Thus he matured in the fantastic fragments and endearing rubble of this ancient empire, and throughout his life his sentimental image of its former glories fed his political ideals. *Lohengrin*, despite elements of the supernatural, preserves and communicates this romantic vision with remarkable immediacy.

The first act curtain rises upon tenth-century Brabant at a point of crisis. It is to be confronted in a very Wagnerian manner: The King of Saxony, Henry the Fowler, but recently arrived, is about to deliver a lecture to the nobles of the Duchy, assembled to hear him on a subject that inflames their emotions—pan-Germanism. When one part of the Reich is in danger, he maintains, so is its entire structure. He asks the leaders of Brabant to join his struggle against the Hungarians menacing the eastern borders of the Reich: "ob Ost, ob West, das gelte allen gleich!" (Wagner, *Gesammelte Schriften*, Vol. 2, p. 66).

With Lohengrin's arrival and his assumption of the crown of Brabant, most of the nobles take up his cause, that of Henry and the Greater Reich. But not all join in the clamor of approval. Four nobles represent the faction opposing the call to arms—"against a foe who has never menaced us?" (*Gesammelte Schriften*, Vol. 2, p. 91), one of them observes—and they are the very four who will attempt the murder of Lohengrin. He makes short work of them, and their downfall symbolizes the inevitable inefficacy of a narrow, local German patriotism. In the final act, to thrilling fanfares, Germans of the westernmost confines of the Reich rally to the banner of Empire, mustering so that they may offer their swords and, if necessary, their lives, for the easternmost, an extravagant Wagnerian fantasy of the First Reich at its finest. Lohengrin, who for domestic reasons finds himself unable to join the expedition he has helped organize, predicts a victory symbolic of a Reich henceforth invincible against dismemberment: "in fernsten Tagen . . . niemals. . . . !" (*Gesammelte Schriften*, Vol. 2, p. 112).

This is very heady, and, indeed, nothing better communicates the turbulence of Wagner's political thinking at the time than the blood-stirring—and to some, frightening—chorus: "Für deutsches Land das deutsche Schwert! So sei des Reiches Kraft bewärt!" (*Gesammelte Schriften*, Vol. 2, p. 107). Clearly the knights had taken careful notes at King Henry's lecture, and, like most academics, he happily receives his material back as a lesson well learned (and, moreover, sharpened by youthful enthusiasm). Mozart might have found himself sympathetic to the patriotism of such a passage, whatever he might have made of its scale and ferment. Here is a Wagner contemplating the future of his country with a passionate but not unreasonable intensity.

The deplorable change in his social and political theorizing began to make its way clearly to the surface immediately after the composition of *Lohengrin* in the essay called "Die Wibelungen; Weltgeschichte aus der Sage." A strange brew, its properties, good and bad, then drained into a pendant work that soon followed—the earliest sketch of the *Ring*'s plot. The essay came into being at the end of August 1848, the scenario the following October.

Here is the point of divergence from Mozart. Here is the contrast between a mind nurtured by the Enlightenment and one fed by the wildly eddying currents of the Romantic century, the first by the essentially well-bred, if at times eccentric, protoromanticism of Sturm und Drang, the second by a romantic nationalism intensified by both the collapse of the French dream of empire and the strong political reaction which then established itself in the German states. The personal, too, enters the comparison: on the one hand a Mozart reluctant to theorize—only for a moment did he contemplate writing a book, seemingly on the relationship between music and the word—and on the other, a Wagner for whom theorizing in prose was becoming a compulsion. Patriotism, Germanism, Francophobia, and anti-Semitism had merged in his mind to form a single concept: a composite Gallo-Semitic evil infected the Reich and could be eradicated by one remedy alone: German art as realized in its ultimate manifestation, in a projected Wagnerian music-drama about Siegfried and the Nibelungen. The idea had grown to theoretical, albeit vaporous, form in "Die Wibelungen," to more solid expression in the scenario for the *Ring*, and would continue to put forth new branches in endless transformations. But it must be kept in mind that on its earliest (and, for many, most profound) level, the *Ring* imposed itself as an allegory of the threatened Reich.

Past midpoint in his almost three decades of struggle to complete the *Ring*, Wagner turned to contemplate afresh his vision of the ancient Reich. Whereas in *Lohengrin* he had implied that the Holy Roman Empire and holy German art partook of the same substance, the more pragmatic Wagner of *Die Meistersinger* turned away from this equation, offering in its place pure nostalgia, an Eden of empire from which the snake has been laughingly tricked. In this mood he could calmly contemplate the collapse of empire, or, if you will, of Valhal, because, as Hans Sachs teaches the German folk: "Were the Holy Roman Empire to dissolve in mist, we would still have our holy German art" (Wagner, *Gesammelte Schriften*, Vol. 7, p. 271). In short, Wagnerian opera would remain Germany's consolation whatever her political fate.

After completing *Die Meistersinger*, Wagner had once again to push forward with the *Ring*, which, ironically, meant returning to a concept, despite changes and tinkering, dating in its essentials from past decades: from the era of "Die Wibelungen," of his mutinous moods during confrontations with Dresden's civil administration, of the turmoil of his flirtation with anarchic communism, of his posturing in Saxony as a socialist revolutionary in politics and aesthetics. Because the basic structure of the *Ring* had been built in Dresden so far in the past and, no less importantly, because he had simultaneously and laboriously put into place an involved politico-aesthetic system upon which, so he proclaimed, the drama would rest, Wagner the theorist found himself trapped in his own prose. Even though his conception of the myth's meaning, of the very destinies of the protagonists, and of his methods of setting their words to music had with the years all utterly changed, to the last note of the *Ring* he persisted in wandering in the bizarre aesthetic labyrinth he had designed decades earlier; despite ingenious attempts, he could never escape its intercommunicating passages. With the distance of nearly a century and a half, let us venture to get at least a bird's eye view of where these passages led and discover why he had arranged them so.

The *Ring* had arisen out of his desire to bring into being a festival drama both ritualistic and celebratory. It was to honor the German socialists who, by the time of the premiere, would have burned down the great capitals of Europe and, yet, somehow survived. (Wagner was not good at details of this kind.) Out of what he called the "fire cure" would rise his new drama (*Die Sammlung Burrell*, p. 775). It was to give the surviving German world a new mythology, resuscitating its ancient gods as symbols so powerful as to put an end to a Christianity he loathed as Judaic error perpetuated. His original vision of the first festival pictured a gathering of socialists, all of them atheists, whom he would summon to a theater built on the banks of the Rhine, the very scene of the action.

The failure of the Dresden uprising, his significant part in it, and the consequent price upon his head compelled him to flee to Switzerland. In Zürich he wrote a series of tracts setting forth his politico-aesthetic tenets. *Art and Revolution* (1849) called for a revolution serving to free Germans from a materialism impeding the emergence in their midst of a great national communal drama, one that would be of no lesser stature than that of the ancient Greeks. *The Art-Work of the Future* (1849) revealed that this new drama would in spirit share the general structure and animating qualities of the ancient model by combining all the arts, but now in a creation satisfying the instinctive needs and intuitive genius of the German folk; *Judaism in Music* (1850) identified the Jews as cultural parasites having no relationship with the German folk, as foreigners incapable of grasping the profundity of this new national expression, as the very group hindering its efflorescence, and, accordingly, as a burden to be cast from German life. *Opera and Drama*

(1851) outlined the devices of the new drama, whose music would proceed from its text, and discussed the role of leitmotif.

Implicit in the Zürich essays lies the concept of the *Ring* as the only possible instrument of German rebirth, of German political and artistic redemption. Wagner looked upon himself as more than the German Aeschylus: he stepped forth as the poet-priest through whose works the unconscious racial genius of the nation would rise to the occasion. He declared the *Ring* poem to be not only the greatest in the language—he fully believed it would replace Goethe's *Faust* as the national epic—but the "greatest ever written" (*Briefe an Theodor Uhlig*, p. 246).

With the promulgation of the Swiss essays, which Liszt's mistress, the cigar-smoking Princess Carolyne Sayn-Wittgenstein, called "grosses bêtises" (Glasenapp, Vol. 2, p. 412), Wagner set himself upon a high pedestal from which, many must have imagined, his fall would be swift and annihilating, especially since the work in question had yet to be revealed, indeed, had yet to be written. Here was a Baptist predicting his own coming; and there could only be speculation about what he would do when he arrived; his prose was vague, indeed, at times intractable.

Upon his miraculous arrival, Lohengrin had solved his immediate problems by issuing stern, stentorian commands that no questions be asked. At least his authority rested upon a publicly applauded act. But what credentials did Wagner have when, late in 1851, he directed a public plea ("A Communication to My Friends") for funds to support his plan to bring before the German folk a musical tragedy based upon Teutonic myth, a composite work with the giant dimensions of three separately performed dramas and a prologue, the whole affair to consume four days?

At the time of the "Communication," apart from Liszt's recent, very small-scaled (and as yet totally uninfluential) premiere production of *Lohengrin* in tiny Weimar (1850), the German theater had not mounted a new work from Wagner's pen in years. It had been six years since *Tannhäuser*, eight since the not terribly successful appearance of *Der Fliegende Holländer*, and nine since his only truly popular opera, *Rienzi*, overwhelmed its first-night Dresden audience. All of these works bore the imprint of Paris and its Opéra. With such creations as a frame of reference, what could potential patrons possibly make of his plan for a Germanic racial drama to be based upon the doings of Siegfried and the Nibelungen, to be presented as a political festival lasting more than half a week, and to have as its goal the regeneration of the Fatherland? Very little, one feels certain.

Yet, it was in the period immediately following the "Communication" that the first significant body of Wagnerian enthusiasts began to gather. They formed the advance guard of those societies which would in time proliferate over Europe. Wagner's Nibelung plan set them astir: the romance of a mighty mythological drama, its wealth of situations to be realized within the framework of a revolutionary festival; the work's pictorial apparatus, which, seemingly, would outdo that of the Paris Opéra itself; and the text, its very latencies offering a mysterious promise, like that of exotic buds awaiting an unknown stimulus—the as yet unwritten music.

Moments of beauty notwithstanding, Wagner's *Ring* text is unendurable without its music. He, of course, conceived the words with a subconscious apprehension of their musical investiture, and one must marvel at his extraordinary histrionic genius and the no less extraordinary patience and devotion of the audiences in Switzerland, public and private, upon whom he inflicted solo readings of the poem before its music had come to paper. Confessing a gospel yet to be written, those first Wagnerites must have been made of strong stuff. Today one cannot glance at a line of the *Ring* without hearing in the inner ear the accompanying music; but, to keep from fleeing the hall, those earliest Wagnerites had only a faith sustained by the magnetic personality that commanded it.

In respect to important cultural figures, Wagner did blunder in printing the text in Zürich (1853) before composing the music that was to vindicate its queerness as a literary work. The so-called poetry, for example, embarrassed Liszt, bewildered Berlioz, and especially disquieted Schopenhauer who read the copy Wagner sent him (Christmas, 1854) and protested against the reckless grammar, convoluted syntax, and improvised vocabulary: "He has no ears, the deaf-music-maker!" observed the sage renowned for his lucidity of expression. On their less exalted level, however, the Faithful remained faithful: they continued to put trust in Wagner's claim that the *Ring*, when finally provided with music realized according to the recipes of *Opera and Drama*, would unveil the single artistic truth for which Germany had longed through the ages, though some of the more perceptive might have been surprised to find themselves mounting guard for a composer who could not compose. He had become musically impotent.

Since completing the *Lohengrin* prelude in August 1847, apart from a few desultory sketches, Wagner had composed nothing. The self-proclaimed hero of modern music could not put a note to paper. He had filled his hours and maintained his grand façade by grinding out the prose of the Swiss essays, cobbling the text of the *Ring*, and seeking relief from imaginary illnesses (and a very real and perennial constipation) in travel, especially to spas. His musical drought lasted six years—it is difficult to think of another major composer who suffered so extended a block—and at times his letters to Liszt, though never acknowledging the problem, betray deep despair. Not until the autumn of 1853, during a sudden violent attack of dysentery in La Spezia, did his musical perceptions sufficiently clear for notations to begin to come to him once again. He returned to Zürich to start the score of *Rheingold*.

The music of the *Ring* did not achieve completion for another twenty-two years: psychological obstructions recurrently brought its progress to a halt. For Wagnerites it had become a blank check, by definition an instrument signed but undated. Yet his followers continued to believe in the promise of a work seemingly endlessly "in progress"; they persevered even in the face of a sudden crisis: the validity of those flinty tablets of the law he had chiseled in Zürich had come dramatically into question.

A pardon for his revolutionary activities had permitted him to return to Germany. He once again put aside the *Ring* and applied his energies to composing *Tristan* (1865) and *Meistersinger* (1868), his first works completed and produced since *Lohengrin*, indeed since the Swiss essays. The aesthetic principles embodied in their prose, the new creations demonstrated, had little, indeed, nothing, to do with his artistic practice: in *Tristan*, he candidly admitted having thrown all theory to the winds; he had, in fact, produced a glorious Lisztean orchestral tone-poem fitted out with vocal obbligati (so much for the dominance of the word!). For its part, *Meistersinger* shamelessly exhibited all the closed Italian forms the essays (in particular, "Opera and Drama") had damned and placed on the Wagnerian Index; the score luxuriated in the forbidden: distinct arias, a love duet, marches in the Spontini-Meyerbeer manner, choruses, elaborate ensembles (even a quintet), and, God help Germany, a ballet in the tradition of vaudeville, the whole marvelous affair enveloping a truly old-fashioned libretto derived from the kind of book Eugene Scribe might have provided the Paris Opéra. A disciple like Nietzsche felt that glorious as the works were, Wagnerian aesthetics had turned out to be something of a joke. Yet there remained the hope that the *Ring* would accommodate the Master's work to his earlier pronouncements and set the Wagnerian world aright.

Das Rheingold and *Die Walküre* had their premières in Munich in 1869 and 1870, respectively, the last two *Ring* operas first reaching the stage in Bayreuth during 1876. Over the years, Wagnerian articles had restated and reiterated the Swiss theories. But, once again, little on stage or in the pit showed fidelity to them. From the heroic duet that closes *Siegfried* to the destruction of Valhalla, the audience experienced a wondrous free rhapsody unfettered by doctrinal restrictions, the atmosphere of these musical outpourings being more redolent of Meyerbeer and the Opéra at their grandest than of Aeschylus. Yet "Opera and Drama" remained the standard by which Wagnerites measured the *Ring;* on the whole they found nothing wanting, for Wagner, insisting that they hear and see according to his injunction, continued to impose belief in the essays, clinging ever more tightly to his robes of infallibility.

Here was one of the most remarkable maneuvers in the career of someone who, since boyhood, had practiced the acrobat's art. Having put forward the master plan of his *Gesamtkunstwerk* and carried it through in a manner at variance with almost every aesthetic point of that plan, he ended by persuading the world that his prospectus had, in fact, been thoroughly and gloriously realized. (To those, like Nietzsche, who raised their eyebrows, he insisted that though everything might seem different, nothing had changed.) Of great aid in this subterfuge was a prose promiscuously mixing political, aesthetic, and moral questions as it effaced the boundaries between the mind and the passions. He singled out few to whom he felt excuses were due: the Wagnerian movement did not as yet include many intellectuals—Nietzsche, the exception, dramatically proving the rule—and one suspects that most in the ranks had not even recognized the philosophic dilemma. Whatever they might make of the Nibelungen project, they wanted to believe in it and in him—or rather, in him, and as a correlative, in it. The success of his grand mystification rested mainly upon the power of a personality of boundless vitality and breathtaking vanity; a personality that imposed itself and carried all before it; that demanded and received; that commanded and compelled; its motto: "Nie sollst du mich befragen."

How deep-seated were these traits? Here I borrow a motto from the Catholic Church: *Sicut erat in principio.*

There is the classic anecdote about Wagner and Schumann: Schumann deplores Wagner's incessent talking, leaving no space for anyone else to wedge in a word, and Wagner complains that Schumann never says very much. They had been acquainted since late adolescence and knew one another very well.

During his brief stay at the university, Wagner became known as the young man who talked *at*, not *to*, others and for his intolerance of views departing from his own. (Though not a psychologist, I venture to associate Wagner's endless harangues, his vehement volubility, with his lifelong penchant for putting on costumes, a tendency reaching from the outrageous uniform he created for himself as a fraternity boy—an outfit that startled the good burgers going about their business in the streets of Leipzig—to the fantastic creations he at times wore in Riga, Vienna, Triebschen, Bayreuth, and even on tour.) From adolescence he cultivated only those who agreed with him and, no less importantly, who reached for the bill. He was proud of his flaring temper, going back to his childhood nickname of "cossack." "I let myself go, and how I did rage," he recalled, recounting his chastising of a young disciple—one Friedrich Nietzsche—who had left a score by Johannes Brahms on the master's piano. One thinks of his first unsuccessful attempt to begin the score of *Tannhäuser*, an ordeal that ended with his smashing the piano in fury. Ludwig of Bavaria was appalled to watch him pounding on the exquisite gilded rococo furniture of the Munich Residenz Palace as he accented his points. Despite his pretensions, he never became truly housebroken and remained the boy from Brühl, the Leipzig ghetto, his accent and manners often a deep embarrassment to those who honored his genius. But this genius had its infinite fascination and exercised a power that held them in thrall.

By the end of his days, he had become a very sick and prematurely old man, fuming endlessly about the French, the Jews, the Jesuits, and their danger to Bismarck's new Reich, which he both admired and hated. To mention names like Mendelssohn, Schumann, Chopin, Brahms, and Verdi was to awaken a volcano. The greater his indebtedness to the composer named, the greater the outburst. Only for Berlioz, alone among those to whom he owed so much, could he find a few kind words.

I have attempted to examine in historical perspective Wagner's excessive nationalism with its related Francophobia and anti-Semitism and to see these tendencies in relationship to his romantic vision of the

Reich; to observe these preoccupations feeding into and becoming part of the fabric of the *Ring* (in many of whose most probing scenes the dialectic of the Reich's redemption and destruction is exhaustively argued); to ponder Wagner's extraordinary belief that his *Ring* and the golden ring of the saga were one and the same: the sole instrument that might lead to national salvation; to outline his elaborate philosophic/ aesthetic program for the execution of this artwork of the future, and to observe how analysis of his manipulation of the theories, no less than the pretensions of the great cycle itself, provides a deep and revealing view of the basis of his personality. I hope that I have to some degree succeeded.

REFERENCES*

Glasenapp, Carl Fr. *Das Leben Richard Wagners.* 6 vols. Leipzig: Breitkopf and Härtel, V.D.
   Abbreviated as Glasenapp.
Mozart, Wolfgang A. *Briefe und Aufzeichnungen: Gesamtausgabe.* Ed. by Wilhelm A. Bauer and Otto Erich Deutsch. 7 vols. Kassel, Basel, London, and New York: Bärenreiter, 1962–75.
   Abbreviated as Mozart, *Briefe.*
Wagner, Richard. *Briefe an Theodor Uhlig, Wilhelm Fischer, Ferdinand Heine.* Leipzig: Breitkopf and Härtel, 1888.
   Abbreviated as *Briefe an Theodor Uhlig.*
—— *Briefe, Die Sammlung Burrell.* Frankfort-on-Main: Fischer, 1953.
   Abbreviated as *Die Sammlung Burrell.*
—— *Gesammelte Schriften und Dichtungen in Zehn Bänden. (Goldene Klassiker-Bibliothek).* Ed. by Wolfgang Golther. 10 vols. Berlin, Leipzig, Vienna, and Stuttgart: Bong, N.D.
   Abbreviated as: *Gessammelte Schriften.*

---

*All quotations come from the following sources; all translations into English are by Robert W. Gutman.

3

The Visual Wagner: Environments, Icons, and Images

Alessandra Comini, Ph.D.

The will to create and the compulsion to destroy, these two, often simultaneous urges characterize the prodigious musical and literary output of Richard Wagner. For sheer lifelong energy and protean self-expression at a mythic level, Wagner the composer-librettist had no parallel in his own century. The twentieth century has responded only with a giant from the visual arts—Pablo Picasso, another creator-destroyer, who, by provoking Cubism, forever changed our ways of accounting for the visible world. Both geniuses provided metaphors for modern times. In doing so, both posed a threat to the cosmic order of things, to the perimeters within which music and art had been systematized. And both men required ambitious physical arenas—villas, even theaters—as inspiration and repository for their vast productions.

As an art historian who is intrigued by the physical evidence at the scene of creativity, and by the icons and images selected to embellish that environment, I am drawn, like a detective with a magnifying glass, to an examination of what, in the context of the present work on the *Ring*, might be called the "visual Wagner." This encompasses Wagner's own widely varying sequence of domiciles, from the freezing, austere flat in Riga of 1837, where the 24-year-old composer sat daily next to two Russian stoves hidden by huge drapes, puffing on a porcelain pipe while working on his opera *Rienzi*, to the sumptuous salon of his final home, Villa Wahnfried in Bayreuth, where, from 1874 onwards, surrounded by his leather-bound volumes and sartorial velvets, the master obligingly received the musical world (Figure 1).

Figure 1. O. Schweninger, *Fantasy Portrait of Wagner at Home in Villa Wahnfried,* detail, c. 1890, oil, present location unknown.

I should like to explore some of these documented Wagner environments, including three royal residences to which he was privy as the guest of his enraptured patron, young King Ludwig II, and to examine them from the viewpoint that what the composer chose to surround himself with—the icons and images essential to his self-image and composing calm—sheds more than passing light on the *Ring* composer's personality and his creative process.

As early as October of 1843, in a spacious Dresden apartment on the Ostra Allée near the silvery Elbe River, close to Semper's dazzling opera house and the great Zwinger palace complex, Kapellmeister Wagner had set up as a household altarpiece, in a "handsome Gothic frame" (his words) over his "stately writing-desk" (again, his words) the copper engraved title page (Figure 2) for *The Nibelungenlied,* designed by the Nazarine artist Peter Cornelius (1783–1867) in 1817 (Wagner,

1911a, p. 505). The only other decoration was an anonymous steel engraved portrait of Beethoven (Figure 3), now preserved in the Wagner Villa Triebschen, near Lucerne. These two images, aptly symbolizing Poetry and Music, would travel with Wagner to each new environment. The six vignettes in Cornelius' crowded title page are somewhat stiff in execution, but charged with histrionic moments, and on the whole this reflects Wagner's appreciation—or actually lack of appreciation—for the visual arts: content rather than style was what mattered to this dramatizer of words and music. Several of Cornelius' *Nibelungenlied* drawings illustrate events that Wagner would incorporate into his *Der Ring des Nibelungen*: we can easily recognize the scene in *Siegfried*, Act I, in which a boisterous Siegfried unleashes the bear he has captured (Figure 4) and, in another drawing, that moment from the prologue to Act I of *Götterdämmerung*, when the love-smitten Siegfried bids farewell to Gutrune to set off with Gunther and Hagen (Figure 5).

The library of some two hundred titles built up by the young Wagner during his seven years as Kapellmeister in Dresden between the ages of 29 and 36, contained (with the exception of the composer's later discovery of Schopenhauer) the kernel and stimulus for every one of his poetic and musical dramas from *Tannhäuser* to *Parsifal*. Pivotal among Wagner's treasures at this time, in addition to the Cornelius *Nibelungenlied* title page, was a copy of Jakob Grimm's *Deutsche Mythologie*, as well as various dictionaries for help in comparing translations of the Icelandic Eddas and Norse Sagas with the original texts, as preparation for the composer's own Nibelung poem.

In the same year that Wagner moved into the Ostra Allée with his icons, Gustav Pfizer's new translation of *The Nibelungenlied* appeared in a deluxe edition with woodcuts after drawings by Julius Schnorr von Carolsfeld (1794–1872). This artist was present two years later at a Dresden reading of Wagner's *Lohengrin* poem to the Dresden *Engelklub*, and we may surmise that at some point Wagner compared Schnorr's version of Siegfried's death (Figure 6) with that of Cornelius (Figure 7).

In Cornelius' picture the murderous Hagen runs off with his crossbow to the right, his terrible deed just accomplished, while on the left Siegfried, already pierced through and through with the fatal arrow in his one vulnerable spot, the back, wheels about in surprise. The cowardly deed is yet to be done in Schnorr's more suspenseful version, which more closely resembles the episode in Act III of *Götterdämmerung*: "Can

Figure 2. Peter Cornelius, title page for the *The Nibelungenlied*, 1817, copper
engraving in Wagner's collection.

Figure 3. Anonymous artist, *Portrait of Beethoven*, c. 1830, steel engraving,
Richard Wagner Museum, Villa Triebschen, Lucerne.

Figure 4. Peter Cornelius, *The Nibelungenlied: Siegfried and the Bear*, 1812–1817, engraving.

Figure 5. Peter Cornelius, *The Nibelungenlied: Siegfried's Parting from Gutrune*, 1812–1817, engraving.

Figure 6. Julius Schnorr von Carolsfeld, *The Niebelungenlied: Hagen Slays Siegfried,* 1843, fresco, Residenz, Munich (destroyed)

Figure 7. Peter Cornelius, *The Nibelungenlied: Siegfried's Murder,* 1812–1817, engraving.

you read the speech of those ravens?'' Hagen asks, and while Siegfried strains to see the birds of flight, the Nibelung's son aims his spear at the hero's back. While Schnorr's dramatic picture precedes Wagner's scene, the artist would become directly involved in Wagnerian imagery when his son, Ludwig Schnorr von Carolsfeld—Wagner's greatest and heftiest Heldentenor—premiered the role of Tristan on June 10, 1865, only to die suddenly of a fever six weeks later. Three years later the grieving father would create a drawing showing his son as Tristan in an attempt to console himself.

No Heldentenor of equal merit graced Franz Liszt's production of his esteemed friend's *Lohengrin* at Weimar in 1850, but Wagner—now a political exile in Switzerland—was so grateful to his colleague for effecting the premiere that soon he was begging to have a "really good" portrait of him, adding: "You need not be ashamed of hanging on my wall; at present I have there only Beethoven, besides the Nibelung design by Cornelius" (Hueffer, 1973, p. 182). And so the Nibelung talisman accompanied Wagner in his peregrinations abroad. We can imagine Richard and his first wife Minna selecting an appropriate place for that icon in the little country house ("asylum") with garden overlooking Lake Zurich, purchased on their behalf by Otto Wesendonck in 1857. A maudlin illustration showing life at "Das Asyl" provided by Liebig's Meat Extract (Figure 8) depicts both the brand new Villa Wesendonck, and the beautiful Mathilde Wesendonck, with whom Wagner was conducting a Tristan-and-Isolde-inspiring affair of the heart inside the garden house, just fifty yards from the composer's open window. As we shall see, the palatial square design (Figure 9) and spacious salon of Villa Wesendonck would leave their imprint upon Wagner's conception of what his own villa and music room of the future should look like. The "Asyl-Idyll" lasted only a year. Minna objected to her husband's latest muse, and Otto finally declined the loan of his wife, and later even his money to the avaricious Richard.

The year 1863 found Wagner permanently separated from Minna and resettled on the entire second floor of a baronial house (the Villa Penzing) near Schloss Schönbrunn in Vienna. Engravings after Raphael—one would end up in the children's room at Wahnfried—and an Erard grand piano completed the furnishings of the music room just in time for the composer's fiftieth birthday, which, in spite of an evening serenade provided by the local Merchants' Choral Society, he celebrated in gloomy spirits, feeling lonely and abandoned.

Figure 8. Anonymous artist, *Life at "Das Asyl,"* Liebig's Meat Extract scene from Wagner's life, c. 1890.

Figure 9. Photograph of the Villa Wesendonck, left, with Wagner's "Das Asyl" garden house on the right, c. 1885.

And then the miracle occurred. The dramatic meeting on the fourth of May 1864 between the two extravagant builders—Ludwig II of castles, Wagner of music dramas—came at a crucial moment in both their lives. The 18-year-old monarch (Figure 10), on the Bavarian throne for only a few weeks, and the 50-year-old musician (Figure 11), now on the run from Austrian creditors after fleeing Vienna to avoid arrest, had been searching for each other for years—Wagner for a king (any king), Ludwig specifically for the composer of the opera about his childhood hero Lohengrin. As a boy in his father's newly renovated, neo-Gothic castle Hohenschwangau on the swan-stocked Alpsee below Munich, he had literally grown up in front of the image of the Swan Knight, as presented in the romantic mural decorating the castle dining room (Figure 12). Eagerly, he memorized the libretti to *Tannhäuser* and *Lohengrin*, saw his first performance of *Lohengrin* when he was 15, then *Tannhäuser* a year later, and the following year, 1863, he read Wagner's *Ring* poem, in the preface of which the composer had expressed his hope that "a prince" would be found to subsidize the *Ring's* production. Crown Prince Ludwig interpreted this as a personal appeal, and fewer than five weeks after ascending the throne, he invited Wagner to come to Munich.

The meeting, which Wagner proudly described as one great love scene, took place in Ludwig's third floor chambers in the Residenz, fronting on one side the Odeonsplatz, with its rococo Theatiner Church and open loggia commemorating Bavarian generals. As he strode through the ground floor of the Residenz, Wagner may well mentally have applauded the prescience involved in the 1827 commission by Ludwig—grandfather of *his* Ludwig—to Julius Schnorr von Carolsfeld to decorate six rooms with monumental frescoes relating to the Nibelungen legends. The contiguous rooms bordering the Max Josephplatz led the visitor from the room of heroes to episodes of betrayal, revenge, and mourning. Across from Ludwig II's private audience room a staircase led down to the second floor where, in Wagner's honor, the young king would soon command that the long corridor beneath his chambers be decorated as a Nibelungen hall. The work was begun in November of 1864 by the painter Michael Echter (1812–1879). Thirty panels with scenes from the *Ring* (Figure 13) were distributed between the fourteen windows and opposite wall that ran along the Residenzstrasse. Wagner made Echter revise his sketches for the hall as many as three times. This first temple to Wagner—Ludwig's Nibelungen Corridor—was destroyed

Figure 10. Colored photograph of Ludwig II at the age of 18, Munich, 1864, presented by Ludwig to Wagner.

Figure 11. Photograph of Richard Wagner at the age of 50, Munich, 1864.

Figure 12. Michael Neher and Lorenz Quaglio, after a design by Christian Ruben, *The Arrival of the Swan Knight*, 1835, fresco, dining room of Castle Hohenschwangau, Füssen.

Figure 13. Michael Echter, *Alberich Stealing the Gold from the Rhine Maidens*, 1864–1865, fresco, Residenz, Munich (destroyed).

in World War II and we know the panels only in copies made by Franz Heigel (1813–1888) around 1865–1866 for Ludwig's favorite summer retreat, Schloss Berg.

It was to this small castle on beautiful Lake Starnberg, twenty miles south of Munich, that the enamored Ludwig lured his obliging idol, renting a capacious rustic villa for him—Haus Pellet—into which the composer moved just ten days after the miracle meeting in Munich. This first, long summer, from May to the end of September, was conducted at fever pitch, as Wagner crowingly reported in letters to confidants: "Daily he sends either once or twice [for me]. Then I fly as to a sweetheart" (Kesting, 1983, p. 494).

For Wagner's fifty-first birthday, on May 22, 1864, Ludwig surprised his cherished new friend with a portrait of himself in general's uniform—a life-size effigy hurriedly painted at the king's command by Friedrich Dürck (1809–1884) (Figure 14). This impressive new icon would henceforth greet visitors to all of Wagner's future residences, and its final resting place at Villa Wahnfried was near a not so easily packable gilded bronze cast of Schloss Hohenschwangau, a little memento from

Figure 14. Friedrich Dürck, *Ludwig II in a Bavarian General's Uniform,* 1864, oil, Villa Wahnfried, Bayreuth.

Ludwig to Wagner. Ludwig desired a return effigy of Wagner (inscribed photographs of the master taken by his court photographer would not satisfy him, see Figure 11) and on August 1st a three-dimensional image in flawless Carrara marble (so specified by the contract) was ordered from the capable young sculptor Caspar Zumbusch (1830–1915), future creator of the great Beethoven Monument in Vienna. (For a discussion of this monument and Wagner's great interest in acquiring [smaller] Beethoven icons for his personal collection see Comini [1987, especially pp. 252–305, 347–387].) Zumbusch hurried to Lake Starnberg to model his subject and by the twenty-fifth of the month—Ludwig's nineteenth birthday—a plaster cast was ready. Old King Ludwig I, who had abdicated the throne in 1848, saw the bust (Figure 15) and complimented the sculptor on the very rich spiritual quality of the head. The enchanted grandson ordered four more copies in smaller, travel size, and in December of the following year Ludwig magnanimously ordered a full-size marble replica made for Wagner's "dear friend" Frau Cosima von Bülow and her husband. With eyes still only for Wagner, Ludwig did not yet perceive, or wish to perceive the sexual dynamics of the Wagner–Frau von Bülow association.

Ludwig could caress his Richards in marble, but the coolness of the stone did not dampen his craving for more visual trophies. He urged Wagner (who had already given away his photographic image of Ludwig to Mathilde Maier) to sit for an oil portrait, and by the end of January of 1865 he had a doubly flattering likeness (Figure 16) to hang in the Residenz alongside images of his ancestors. Wagner's portrait painter friend from Paris and Dresden days, Friedrich Pecht (1814–1903), had conceived, as noted in Wagner's explanatory letter to Ludwig, the happy idea of introducing a bust of the young king into the painting, the presence of which triggered the "calmly reflective" expression on the inspired composer's face. The "beloved protector's" idealized marble bust was the work of none other than Caspar Zumbusch, who had completed the head just a few months earlier. Later, Ludwig would endow Wagner with a twice-as-large bronze version of the bust for placement outdoors at Villa Wahnfried. Naturally it was Ludwig, not Wagner, who absorbed the costs for all these icons.

Before we leave Schloss Berg, happy witness to those first charmed months of the royal friendship, let us make a brief circuit of this unusual trysting point. Ludwig added a north entrance tower in honor of the event, bestowing upon it, in pre-Freudian innocence, the name

Alessandra Comini

Figure 15. Caspar Zumbusch, *Ludwig II*, 1864, marble, Villa Wahnfried, Bayreuth.

Figure 16. Friedrich Pecht, *Richard Wagner with the Bust of Ludwig II*, 1865, oil, The Metropolitan Museum of Art, New York.

"Isolde." The top story contains the corner study-salon where the composer visited his king. To enhance and perpetuate the memory of Wagner's presence in this room Ludwig ordered Zumbusch back to work, carving in marble heroes from Wagner operas to keep him company (Figure 17). From left to right are the figures of Tristan, Lohengrin (at Ludwig's request, the first to be carved), and Tannhäuser. Ludwig also commissioned the artist Eduard Ille (1823–1900) to provide him with authentic scenes from Wagner's source, the Niflunga-Saga. The ambitious table of contents results were displayed on the walls in black frames. Zumbusch created six statuettes in all, each with recognizable attributes—Lohengrin with his friendly swan, Siegfried with his sword and hunting horn. The other figures would be the Flying Dutchman, Walther von Stolzing, and later, Parsifal. Eventually, Ludwig would supply Wagner with marble replicas of all six figures (preserved at Villa Wahnfried).

Of greater practical use to Wagner was the mansion provided by Ludwig back in Munich at the end of the summer honeymoon—the Hôtel Jochum on the city's elegant Briennerstrasse, not far from the Residenz and right next to the magnificent Königsplatz with its Glyptothek museum and brand new Propylaea. Not a bad neighborhood. Although Wagner quickly filled the house with his usual Erard grand piano, velvet hangings, and the von Bülow clan, what he remembered later about the villa, as he wrote Ludwig, was the small garden with peacocks wandering around in it.

Not only peacocks but swans greeted Wagner when he visited Ludwig for the first time at Schloss Hohenschwangau on August 25, 1864, to congratulate him on his birthday. Ludwig's third-floor apartment contained the music room with the square, maple-wood piano upon which Wagner played nuggets from the Nibelung for his adoring audience of one, and the bay-window room looking out onto the castle garden in which he slept during his second, week-long visit to Hohenschwangau in November of the following year. His first morning there Wagner was awakened at dawn by an aubade of themes from *Lohengrin*, played from the castle turrets by oboists from the king's First Infantry regiment.

But this would be Wagner's last visit to Ludwig's castle. The combination of fiscal greed and blatant adultery on the composer's part obliged Ludwig most reluctantly to bow to public outrage and to rid Bavaria of its controversial guest artist at the end of 1865. This forced

Figure 17. Anonymous artist, *Ludwig II in his Study at Schloss Berg,* c. 1865–1870, oil, present location unknown.

Figure 18. Photograph of Wagner's Villa Triebschen, Lucerne, c. 1870, after renovations.

the composer back into exile and Switzerland was once again his choice. Zurich and the Wesendonck compound were now out of the question (Cosima, still legally married to von Bülow, had given birth to her first child by Richard in April), but a lake-with-mountains locale of equal beauty was offered by Lucerne, and it was there that Wagner discovered what he was pleased to call the Villa Triebschen (Figure 18). Beautifully situated on a hilly tongue of land overlooking the lake and town of Lucerne, everything was right about the house except its deteriorating condition. Ludwig's generous renovation money (in addition to rent money) would soon fix that, however, and the Triebschen house became the happy home to Wagner's growing family for the next six years. The garden was soon stocked with peacocks and, unable to contain his long-ing for the hero who had been driven out of his kingdom, Ludwig himself appeared at the front door as a birthday surprise for Wagner on May 22, 1866—just five weeks after the composer himself had moved into the house! The King of Bavaria had announced himself as *Die Meistersinger's* Walther von Stolzing, and back in Munich he made sure that his "beloved friend" was kept supplied not only with Zumbusch statuettes but also copies of the Nibelungengang images.

Three years later, responding to Ludwig's query, Wagner described the disposition of his icons and images at Villa Triebschen: in his bed-room hung the king's large photograph and a watercolor of Hohen-schwangau (preferable to a bronze model). In the salon, "now decorated exclusively with oil paintings," Ludwig's portrait was flanked by the images of three equal notables (not Wagner's precise wording): Goethe, Schiller, and Wagner's stepfather, as well as the Zumbusch busts of Ludwig and Wagner. A long hall, grandly called the "gallery," featured six hand-colored photographs based on Michael Echter's *Rhein-gold* scenes (Kesting, 1983b, pp. 743–744). What Wagner did not men-tion, but what we can still see at Triebschen today, was his little portrait gallery of musicians: Gluck, Haydn, Mozart, and Beethoven—small steel engraved portrayals in heavy gold frames—and his own lavish collection of silk shirts and housecoats.

Triebschen was also the environment where the love of Cosima and Richard could at last be legitimized; a few weeks after the divorce from Hans von Bülow came through the couple was married on August 25, 1870. We can again thank the anonymous artist for Liebig's Meat Extract for immortalizing the well-known episode of the staircase (Figure 19) when Richard conducted the early morning musical surprise (the *Siegfried Idyll*) for Cosima on her forty-fourth birthday, Christmas day, 1870. Wagner is shown wearing the "fearsomely large" Flemish-painter-style black velvet beret he called his "Wotan hat" (now on display at Villa Triebschen) and Cosima holds in her arms their six-month-old son Siegfried, who already aspires to conduct (Kesting, 1983b, p. 744). The composer ordered images of the fertile woman who had given him a male heir: a marble bust from the Dresden sculptor Gustav Kietz (1824–1908) (creator of the Goethe-Schiller Memorial in Weimar) and portraits in oil from Franz von Lenbach (1836–1904). Munich's most successful and expensive portrait painter, Lenbach would become a good friend of the Wagners, celebrating Richard and his "Wotan" hat in skillfully rendered Rembrandt tonalities that emphasized the largeness of the composer's head (Figure 20).

Although he eventually lost his admiration for Wagner the man, Ludwig never ceased to worship Wagner the composer, and another royal environment became the backdrop for a tryst arranged on the occasion of Wagner's fifty-fifth birthday. The two men sailed on the little steamer Ludwig had inherited from his father (and which on Wagner's fifty-second birthday he had rechristened the *Tristan*) to a rustic residence on Lake Starnberg's tiny Roseninsel, where 15,000 roses greeted the slender Siegfried and his diminutive Wotan. But the mutual ecstasy of the summer of 1864 was never to be repeated. Politics and pragmatism had intervened. Maudlin posthumous images to the contrary, the Leitmotifs of Ludwig and Wagner were never again to blend so harmoniously. Even in their comprehension and use of the ancient saga that had drawn them together, philosophical differences emerged. Ludwig cared more for history and archaeological exactitude; Wagner more for what would work as universal music drama.

When in 1868 the disillusioned Ludwig realized he could no longer possess Wagner in person, he began to plan his most ambitious fantasy, construction of the castle Neuschwanstein, to be decorated inside as a "temple" to Wagner, a temple into which, as fate would have it, the creator of the *Ring* would never set foot. By 1879, however, when the murals were at last underway, the king commanded that the Nibelung pictorial schemes adhere not to Wagner but to ancient legends. To live to see Wagner's Nibelung, then to die—this had been Ludwig's childhood wish. But now, screening his soul behind a hirsute exterior as he put on weight, his ardent desire was to *dwell* in the world of the Nibelung:

Figure 19. Anonymous artist, *Villa Triebschen: Wagner Directs the Siegfried Idyll on the Stairway for Cosima's Birthday,* Liebig's Meat Extract scene from Wagner's life, c. 1890.

Figure 20. Franz von Lenbach, *Richard Wagner,* December, 1871, oil on wood, Richard Wagner Museum, Villa Triebschen, Lucerne.

at his Linderhof castle he even built himself a replica of Hunding's hut from Act I of *Die Walküre*, hoping perhaps to encounter Siegfried there.

While Ludwig retreated from the hurtful present, Wagner used the past to defy history. Who could remember the Napoleonic humiliations when the glorious voice of Siegfried sounded? How fitting that *Die Walküre* was premiered in the very year that Krupp cannons would decide the Franco-Prussian War in favor of Germany. The two Ludwigs had both built Valhallas to honor history's heroes: Ludwig I gave his country a classical temple high on a hill; Ludwig II, a pastiche medieval castle on an even higher hill. But it would be Wagner's Valhalla, in the form of his Bayreuth festival theater, that, with a sensuous appeal unleavened by history or logic, would present the seductive myths in which Germany yearned to recognize itself. "Vollendet das ewige Werk" ("completed is the immortal work"), Wagner could sing along with Wotan.

Let us descend on Bayreuth now and examine the private Valhalla palace Wagner began constructing in 1872 for himself and his family, the Villa Wahnfried. This was the first time Wagner was able to begin from scratch (thanks again to Ludwig's continued financial aid), and he devised a simple but stately plan (Figure 21). The core of the house was twofold: first, facing the front of the house, a great hall, which served as a rehearsal and concert room and which dwarfed its Villa Wesendonck prototype as it rose through a low mezzanine and balconied upper floor all the way to the glass skylights of the roof. Beyond it was the second great feature, the drawing room or *salon* (Wagner's term), lower than the hall but of greater width and length—a little over 1000 square feet in fact—and culminating in a magnificent five-bay rotunda, the bow windows and center French door of which opened onto the back garden.

The house's square plan, elevation, and projecting entrance-facade (Figure 22) did indeed owe something to Otto Wesendonck's Zurich villa, but the allegorical sgraffito panel by the Leipzig-based portrait painter Robert Krausse (1834–1903)—whom Wagner forbade to use the word *colossal* one more time at the dinner table—was entirely original. The iconography was typically Wagnerian—Cosima's contribution. It shows the union of classical tragedy and Germanic myth with music and the future, as personified by the singers Wilhelmine Schröder-Devrient as antique drama, on the left, and Ludwig Schnorr von Carolsfeld as the wandering Wotan in the center. On the right, two nonsingers, Cosima and her son Siegfried, represent music and the future. "Here where

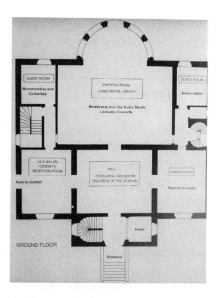

Figure 21. Ground-plan of Villa Wahnfried, Bayreuth.

Figure 22. Photograph of the facade of Villa Wahnfried with Zumbusch's bust of Ludwig in front, 1874, Bayreuth.

my illusions found peace, be this house named by me, 'Peace from Illusion'—Wahnfried," reads Wagner's lumbering inscription across the facade. The visual ensemble was completed in July of 1875 when Zumbusch's bust of Ludwig, now cast in living bronze, arrived at Bayreuth. Just as Ludwig was never to enter Villa Wahnfried, so, symbolically, does his bust turn away from the house.

A rare early photograph (Figure 23) documents which icons and images dwelt in the great hall. To the left was Kietz's bust of Cosima; gazing toward it on the opposite side of the room was Zumbusch's head of Richard. Flanking the doorway were Zumbusch's marble statuettes: Siegfried on the left, Tristan on the right, and further to the right, Lohengrin. Overhead ran a frieze designed by Cosima with a Scandinavian snake motif on a gold background into which were set the watercolor copies ordered by Ludwig for Wagner of Echter's thirty panels for the Munich Residenz Nibelungengang. (In 1945 a bomb struck Villa Wahnfried and destroyed the entire back of the house: restoration was completed in 1976 and most of the original icons and images are back in place.)

A contemporary watercolor of the salon (Figure 24) records its proud possessor, decked out in his velvet Wotan beret and admiring the garden view. Proudly, the new house owner wrote the builder of Neuschwanstein, Linderhof, and Herrenchiemsee that his large salon was a "source of amazement for all . . . this room holds all my possessions: the paneling around the walls contains my collection of books [about 2500 volumes, all bound in leather and filling bookcases against three walls]; our paintings are hung above them . . . the grand piano is over there, and over here is my large desk . . . . " (Spencer and Millington, 1988, p. 839).

Another contemporary watercolor (Figure 25) shows the opposite side of the room with the, as yet undecorated ceiling panels, and the (excessively framed) portraits mentioned by Wagner. All by Lenbach, they are from left to right: Liszt, complete with warts, Cosima, life-size, in three-quarter length, frontal, and dressed in black, and Richard in "sharp and energetic" profile (Cosima's words), looking left. We can also see the low cupboards for papers and documents which ran around the room underneath the bookcases. It was Cosima's idea to decorate the salon ceiling panels with the coats of arms of those cities boasting successful Wagner societies. It is not only tempting but instructive to

Figure 23. Photograph of the great hall, Villa Wahnfried, Bayreuth, c. 1874.

Figure 24. Susanne Schinkel, *Richard Wagner in his Salon at Villa Wahnfried*, c. 1880, watercolor, present whereabouts unknown.

compare this overwrought salon with the sumptuous, justly famous Vienna studio of Wagner's flamboyant painter friend Hans Makart (1840–1884), whose name had become synonymous with a new lavish style of interior decorating, the Makartstil (Figure 26).

In 1875 the Wagners had attended Makart's annual costume party, held in the tropical-Teutonic setting of his atelier (even Sarah Bernhardt had paid a visit to this, the Austrian capital's newest tourist attraction), and it is not surprising that some of Makart's practical shortcuts to environmental magnificence (potted palms, oriental rugs) were appropriated by the receptive couple, always alert to interior decoration ideas. But a parallel can be contemplated on another level as well. The sensuous historical and mythological icons that oozed from Makart's Venetian-Rubensian brush offered the same compelling, unsettling combination as did Wagner's music—*erotica through exotica.*

Wagner required fine silks and satins to compose his sensual music, but his salon could comfortably host art of the most common cloth. The amateur painter Paul von Joukowsky (1845–1912), who was to design the scenery for *Parsifal,* provided a large, ungainly depiction of *The Holy Family* (Figure 27), as mimed by the Bülow and Wagner children for Christmas of 1881. Truly a family icon, the "holy" family is represented by—moving clockwise from lower left—Siegfried as an industrious young carpenter Christ child, Eva, Isolde, and Blandine as bland musical angels, and a reverent Daniele as Mary. At the far right the bearded artist himself makes a modest appearance as Joseph. The painting was afforded a place of honor in the salon. A contemporary photograph (Figure 28), shows it suspended from above the bookshelves behind the grand piano and near Joukowsky's full-length, rather wooden, frontal portrait of Cosima to the right. To the left is Lenbach's picture of Cosima dressed in black and next to it, on the far left, is Lenbach's Wotan-beret portrait of Wagner. The couple were symbolically linked by a massive pair of beveled gold frames which Wagner decided made the "pictures invisible" (Gregor-Dellin and Mack, 1980, p. 573). Directly above the Joukowsky portrait on the wall behind the far bookcases can be seen an icon highly treasured by the composer, the portrait of his much-admired uncle Adolf Wagner as a young man, painted by Wagner's stepfather, the actor and portrait painter Ludwig Geyer (1779–1821). To the far right is Robert Krausse's copy of J. F. A. Tischbein's 1806 portrait of Schiller, the original of which was owned by the Leipzig Schiller Society. Out of sight on the continuation of this wall to

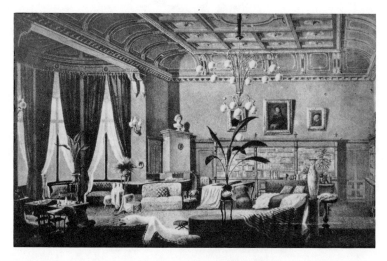

Figure 25. Anonymous artist, *The Salon at Villa Wahnfried*, c. 1876, watercolor, present location unknown.

Figure 26. Rudolf von Alt, *Hans Makart's Studio*, 1885, watercolor, Historisches Museum der Stadt Wien, Vienna.

Figure 27. Paul von Joukowsky, *The Holy Family*, 1881, oil, Villa Wahnfried, Bayreuth.

Figure 28. Photograph of the salon, Villa Wahnfried, Bayreuth, c. 1882.

the right hung another triad of icons, including portraits by Lenbach of Goethe and Liszt.

So pleased was Wagner with Krausse's replica of the Schiller portrait (already in his possession at Lucerne) that he had, while still at Villa Triebschen, arranged for the same artist to copy a much holier icon—the hallowed image of Beethoven. Liszt had hung the famous lithographic portrait of Beethoven by August von Klöber (1793–1864) in his Weimar music rooms for years; now (1869) Wagner would do his attention-attracting father-in-law one better and commission an original oil facsimile. But not of Klöber's tempestuous, tossed-locks Beethoven. No! Wagner had in mind Ferdinand Georg Waldmüller's (1793–1865) famous and grimly objective image of the aging Beethoven (Figure 29). And how completely Wagner approved of Krausse's careful replica, praising it as unaffected and real (Figure 30). And yet, as we look at it today, it is clear that the copy could never be confused for the original. It was through the subjective spectacles of romanticism that both Krausse and Wagner unconsciously saw their Beethoven. His silver-streaked hair, incipient frown, pug nose, and compressed lips have all been—almost involuntarily—enhanced and even exaggerated. This icon clarified, as it were, the impress of suffering and heroic mental activity, aspects with which Wagner could sincerely identify. That Wagner yearned to possess his own icon of the great composer is consonant with his genuine conviction that he was the real and only spiritual heir of Beethoven (For more on this specific aspect of Wagner's hero worship, see Comini [1987, pp. 295–297]).

An arresting image conveying what it was like to be inside Bay-reuth's inner sanctum with the master and his clan is Wilhelm Beck-mann's (1852–1942) painting of 1882, ingenuously titled *Life at Villa Wahnfried* (Figure 31). The scene takes place in Cosima's private sitting room—the "lilac salon," situated to the left of the front door entry into the great hall on the ground floor of the house. A pecking order is clearly delineated. Compositionally and psychologically central, the elegantly attired Wagner-Wotan stands in a Makart-like, potted-palmed salon acknowledging both sides of the room with his extended arms. He listens attentively (ever ready to intervene) while, on the right, a snow-haired Liszt leans forward to expound some fine point of a (most probably Wagnerian) score, not to his son-in-law, but to his spellbound daughter Cosima, who sits erectly on the left, her hand supporting her chin. She is dressed in an elaborately detailed white silk gown similar to the

Figure 29. Ferdinand Georg Waldmüller, *Portrait of Beethoven,* 1823, oil, formerly possession of Breitkopf and Härtel, Leipzig (destroyed).

Figure 30. Robert Krausse, *Copy of Ferdinand Georg Waldmüller's Portrait of Beethoven,* 1869, oil, formerly Villa Wahnfried, Bayreuth.

Figure 31. Wilhelm Beckmann, *Life at Villa Wahnfried*, 1882, oil, Richard Wagner Museum, Villa Triebschen, Lucerne.

one shown in a second life-size portrait of her by Lenbach, which—conveniently for comparison's sake—stands on the table behind her. Yet another "disciple" has been admitted to the inner sanctum: to the far right, sitting in reverential attention next to Liszt, is the young, well-brought-up Hans von Wolzogen, energetic editor of Wagner's publicity organ, the *Bayreuther Blätter*. One further icon has been admitted into Villa Wahnfried. Immediately above Wagner's head, like a halo, is Lenbach's deification—commissioned by the composer—of yet another Wagner hero, Arthur Schopenhauer. "Now at last I could understand my Wotan," Wagner had written in his autobiography, concerning his discovery of the articulator of redemption through renunciation in the autumn of 1854 (Wagner, 1911b, p. 604). In addition to one idol and three disciples, the Beckmann painting shows a Wagner benefactor: on the other side of the French windows, gracing the villa's front entrance garden, Zumbusch's huge bronze bust of King Ludwig appears to be listening approvingly to the musical discussion within this earthly Valhalla. One other item beckons our attention in Wagner's velvety ambiance as documented by Beckmann. Prominently displayed on the floor

behind Cosima is the freshly painted, not-yet-framed canvas executed
by Max Brückner (1836–1919) in 1882 of Joukowsky's Siena-inspired
design for the Temple of the Grail in *Parsifal*. That Wagner's operas
invaded Wagner's villa is no surprise; the great hall had been conceived
to accommodate rehearsals after all.

Perhaps the most illustrious omnium gatherum of all took place in
the great salon: a reception on the occasion of the second Bayreuth
Festspiel in 1882, recorded by the artist George Papperitz (1846–1918)
(Figure 32). Dominating the scene are, reading clockwise from the left,
Cosima with her shy Siegfried and the latest ubiquitous family dog,
Wagner with his beret and open *Ring* score, and Liszt, obligingly playing
from a second *Ring* score at the grand piano. Lenbach is seated to the
far left, behind Cosima, and next to Wagner in front of the window
are Joukowsky and the conductor Hermann Levi. Other musicians and
society ladies abound, and insistently in attendance as well is the painted
presence of Ludwig on the wall behind Liszt (Figure 33). This imposing
image of the now bearded and mustached king as a Knight of the Hubertus Order had been provided by the ever-complaisant Lenbach in
1870, and certainly served as Wagner's most impressive and inescapable icon.

"If I am Wotan, then he is my Siegfried," Wagner had boasted to inti-
mates about "his boy" Ludwig in 1864 (he also wrote Ludwig directly
in this vein, see Spencer and Millington [1988, p. 627]). We have seen
that the protagonists of the *Nibelungenlied* formed a common backdrop
for Ludwig and for Wagner long before they met. For years both had
been indebted to the Nibelungen Saga for the inspired flights of fancy
in which Ludwig took refuge and from which Wagner was fashioning
his tetralogy of creation and destruction. In the "contest" for the golden
ring of Nibelungen imagery it would seem that Ludwig's amassing of it
in pictorial form was an escape from the political realities of a nineteenth-century Germany in which Bavaria would have to submit to Prussian dominance. Wagner's reconstruction of Teutonic myths as music
drama however became the new reality in which contemporary Germany
could not only find but redeem itself, were it but willing, as in the *Ring*,
to destroy the old cosmic order.

Figure 32. George Papperitz, *Richard Wagner in the Circle of His Friends at Villa Wahnfried,* c. 1875, lithograph after the original oil painting.

Figure 33. Franz von Lenbach, *Ludwig II as a Knight of the Hubertus Order,* 1870, oil, Villa Wahnfried, Bayreuth.

REFERENCES

Comini, A. (1987), *The Changing Image of Beethoven: A Study in Mythmaking.* New York: Rizzoli.

Gregor-Dellin, M., & Mack, D., Eds. (1980), *Cosima Wagner's Diaries,* Vol. 1, tr. G. Skelton. New York: Harcourt, Brace, Jovanovich.

Hueffer, F., Trans. (1973), *Correspondence of Wagner and Liszt,* Vol. 1. New York: Vienna House.

Kesting, H., Ed. (1983a), *Richard Wagner Briefe,* Vol. 1. Munich: Piper.

—— (1983b), *Richard Wagner Briefe,* Vol. 2. Munich: Piper.

Spencer, S., & Millington, B., Trans. & Eds. (1988), *Selected Letters of Richard Wagner.* New York: W. W. Norton.

Wagner, R. (1911a), *My Life,* Vol. 1. London: Constable & Company.

—— (1911b), *My Life,* Vol. 2. London: Constable & Company.

4

Richard Wagner and the Problem of German Identity

David Clay Large, Ph.D.

With characteristic modesty, Richard Wagner claimed in 1865: "I am the most German being, I am the German spirit. Note the incomparable magic of my works, compare them with the rest—and you have to say—they are *German*" (R. Wagner, *Brown Book*, p. 73).

Wagner has generally been taken at his word; certainly few figures in the cultural life of Germany have been considered more intensely *German* than Richard Wagner. Yet now, with the reunification of Germany, it might be salutary to look once again at Wagner's relationship with his native land, to examine both his sense of German identity and the ways in which his country has identified with him. If nothing else, I think we will see that the relationship between Germany and one of its most celebrated composers has been much more complicated, more ambiguous, than Wagner's claim would suggest.

Wagner began to think about what it meant to be German when in the mid-1830s he fell under the influence of Young Germany, a radical literary and political movement which advocated the unification of Germany as a democratic republic. Like his colleagues, Wagner believed that the division of Germany into a myriad of separate states, most of which were ruled by very conservative princes, dukes, or bishops, was inimical to the development of a strong and self-confident German culture. Under the domination of their reactionary princes, said Wagner, German artists tended to produce works that were either stuffily parochial or slavishly imitative of foreign (particularly French) models.

In his first published piece of musical criticism, a short article called "German Opera" that appeared in 1834 (Wagner, 1911), Wagner insisted that German composers had to be prepared to learn from the French and Italians, for contemporary German opera—the works of, say, Weber or Spohr—lacked sensuality, warmth, and the beauty of song. Yet Wagner believed that the purpose of this cultural borrowing should be to free the German spirit from its parochial and pedantic stuffiness, so that it could realize its full potential—a German art that combined song and sensuality with profundity and depth of feeling.

It was clear from his earliest writings that Wagner coupled his own prosperity as an artist with the larger political and cultural fate of Germany—a connection he was to persist in making throughout his life. Certainly he felt diminished and constrained on the narrow stage of his native Saxony, especially since he considered his fellow Saxons a bunch of loutish brutes. "They are," he wrote, "an accursed people, these Saxons, greasy, paunchy, ill-bred, lazy and coarse—what have I to do with them?" (Altmann, 1927a, p. 81).

Since the German states lacked a great musical as well as political center at this time, Wagner went to Paris to pursue his destiny as a German artist. Living as a voluntary exile in the French capital, Wagner, like exiles the world over, was pressed to think more deeply about his native country and culture. On the one hand, he continued to brood about the cultural disadvantages of political disunity, complaining that a disunified Germany meant that few German artists could become known beyond the boundaries of any one duchy or principality. It meant, too, that even that most "German" of all arts, namely music, would remain localized. "Thus," he wrote, "we have Prussian, Swabian, and Austrian folksongs, but no truly national musical idiom. As long as Germany remains decentralized, no great musical piece of nation-wide significance will appear" (R. Wagner, 1842, cited in Jacobs and Skelton, 1973, p. 39). At the same time, however, Wagner believed that Germany's lack of political unity and a national musical tradition meant that it had the capacity to create works of art which could transcend national boundaries and encompass all of humanity. Only Germany provided an environment where art could remain uncorrupted by political or material considerations. He wrote:

> It is almost as though the German genius were destined to seek from its neighbors what it did not inherit from its motherland and

to lift what it takes out of its narrow boundaries and provide something universal for the whole world. Naturally this can only be achieved by one who is not content merely to counterfeit a foreign nationality but who preserves pure and uncorrupted the endowment of his Germanic birth, namely genuineness of expression and purity of invention [R. Wagner, 1841, cited in Jacobs and Skelton, 1973, p. 45].

Clearly Wagner thought he was this kind of cosmopolitan German.

Wagner returned to Saxony in 1842 after having failed to find fame and prosperity in Paris. According to an "Autobiographical Sketch" he published the following year, his return was an emotional one. "I saw the Rhine for the first time; with tears swelling in my eyes I, a poor artist, swore eternal loyalty to my German fatherland" (Wagner, 1843, cited in Barth, 1975, p. 16). The sight of the medieval Wartburg Castle, where the mastersingers had held their festivals, where Luther had translated the Bible, and where nationalistic student fraternities had demonstrated for German unity, also excited him; and of course he would eventually transform this scene into the stage picture for Act III of *Tannhäuser*.

Wagner's appointment as Kapellmeister at the court of the Saxon king in Dresden allowed him to produce three of his operas, *Rienzi*, *Der Fliegende Holländer*, and *Tannhäuser*, but he soon became terribly frustrated with the working conditions in Dresden, with the restrictions on his creativity and artistic freedom that he blamed on the influence of a reactionary court camarilla. Thus it is not surprising that when the revolutions of 1848 began sweeping across Europe, including the German states, Wagner welcomed this upheaval as an opportunity both for Germany's national liberation from princely particularism, and for his own liberation as an artist. Later, when he was trying to gain a royal pardon so that he might return to Germany from his exile in Switzerland, he tried to minimize his involvement in the revolutionary events in Saxony. In fact, however, he was very much in the thick of things. He joined a liberal nationalist organization called the Vaterlandsverein, before which he delivered an impassioned speech calling for the creation of a Saxon republic, but one headed, incongruously enough, by the Saxon king, who would become "the first and truest Republican of all" (Millington, 1988, p. 34). Wagner's seemingly bizarre proposal for a monarchist republic reflected his desire, typical among bourgeois liberals of the time, to maintain order in the midst of change, and to preclude the complete triumph of the radical-leftist working-class movement, which he instinctively distrusted. Wagner's nationalism, in other words, did not include an identification with or idealization of the German masses, whom he considered brutish and unenlightened. However, when it became apparent that the Saxon king would not play his appointed role as first Republican, that instead of accepting a new national constitution he would invite Prussian troops into Saxony to crush the rebellion, Wagner threw all caution to the winds and proposed the arming of the populace. Apparently he even instructed a local brass foundery in the manufacture of hand grenades; and when Prussian troops invaded Dresden, he climbed the tower of the *Kreuzkirche* to help coordinate the rebels' hopeless defense.

It was during these heady days of revolution that Wagner began drafting the first prose sketches for his most ambitious work, *Der Ring des Nibelungen*. Much later, when he had fallen under the influence of the racial theorist Count Arthur de Gobineau, Wagner insisted that the *Ring* was "without doubt the Aryan race's most characteristic work of art. . . . " He said it reflected the fact that "no nation on earth could be so clearly conscious of its origins and predispositions as this one tribe from Central Asia, a tribe which was the last to enter European culture and which until that time retained its purity better than all the other white races" (Millington, 1988, p. 914).

This statement is characteristic of Wagner's tendency to reinterpret his art according to his changing political predispositions. The original impulse behind the *Ring* had nothing to do with Aryan race theory or the Germanic chauvinism that characterized Wagner's worldview in his later years. The most important philosophical influences on the first draft were Hegel and Feuerbach, in whose works Wagner found theoretical ammunition for his belief in the possibility of improving humanity through revolutionary change. The main themes explored in the *Ring* were essentially universal. Hegel's influence was evident in the work's development of the dialectical relationship between reason and passion; that is, the certainty that rational actions would produce consequences that were unforeseen, but part of a larger progressive design; and the notion that there was a correspondence between the rational, self-serving acts of individuals and historical necessity. As one critic has aptly noted, Wagner originally conceived Siegfried, then Brünnhilde, as Hegelian "instruments of a purpose which represents a stage in the progress of the universal spirit" (Windell, 1976, p. 29). When he was revising the

Ring in the mid-1850s, Wagner came strongly under the influence of Arthur Schopenhauer, whose pessimistic philosophy of resignation and renunciation, whose vision of the world as a representation or mirror of the primal, blind, all-powerful Will, led him to recast his work in a more psychological, and ultimately more pessimistic, vein. But the central message remained a universal rather than a specifically German one: that the lust for power and the compromises and alliances we are forced to make in our lives threaten our capacity for true, selfless love.

As Wagner was working on the early sketches of the *Ring*, he also began thinking about producing this ambitious work in a novel festival framework, for he was convinced that his new drama could never be adequately realized on the traditional stage and within the conditions of any existing theater. Though he was eventually to try to cast this festival concept as a kind of cultural equivalent to imperial German power and conquest, his first plan, drafted in 1850, called for the *Ring's* production in a plain wooden theater to be erected in a meadow near Zurich, whence Wagner had fled after the failure of the 1848–1849 revolution. The 10,000 talers Wagner thought necessary for this project could be provided by some rich patron; the singers and musicians would donate their services; the guests would pay nothing; the atmosphere would be informal and festive, though full of high idealism; and after the performance Wagner would pull down the building and burn his score. A year later Wagner had slightly revised this scheme, though his plan remained a far cry from what finally transpired in Bayreuth in 1876. Now, in 1851, he spoke of producing the *Ring* in Germany, but only after a revolution had transformed the German political and cultural landscape.

> The coming Revolution must necessarily put an end to this whole *theatrical business* of ours; that must all perish, and will certainly do so, it is inevitable. Out of the ruins I shall then summon together what I need; I shall then find what I require. I shall run up a theater on the Rhine and send out invitations to a great dramatic festival: after a year's preparation I shall then perform my entire work within the space of *four days: with it* I shall then make clear to the men of the Revolution *the meaning* of that Revolution, in its noblest sense. *This audience* will understand me; present day audiences cannot [Millington, 1988, p. 234].

Clearly, the understanding that Wagner hoped to convey with his festival remained at this point rooted in the radical humanist message of his *Ring* drama.

Wagner refined his plan for the production of the *Ring* yet again in the first published edition of the poem in 1862, two years after the Saxon king had granted him a partial amnesty that enabled him to think of returning permanently to Germany. He now spoke of holding his festival in some small German town just large enough to accommodate visitors, but without a theater of its own. Again, the performers would work simply for the honor of participation, and the guests would pay nothing. Gone, however, was the notion that the *Ring* would be staged as a populist celebration of a German revolution that had cleansed the nation of oppressive princes, feudal aristocrats, and culturally reactionary court musical directors. Now that Wagner was trying to facilitate his return to a Germany still dominated by princes and aristocrats, he advertised his festival scheme as a milestone in new German art, but not in new German politics. Accordingly, he now suggested that the production of the *Ring* might best be financed by some German prince who had become disgusted with the imported repertories of his court opera house. Who, asked Wagner in 1862, might this prince be?

Even so self-confident a man as Wagner could not have expected his Maecenas to appear so quickly, or to embrace his art so fervently, as in fact occurred. In 1864 young King Ludwig II ascended the throne of Bavaria and, as is well known, immediately called Wagner to Munich. Ludwig proved more than willing to help Wagner realize his dream of his own theater. He promised to build him a glorious new Festspielhaus on the banks of the Isar, and to provide him with the best artists and technicians in the country.

Happily moving to Munich, Wagner now pronounced himself a Bavarian patriot, claiming to see in that state and its lovely capital the true center of the German spirit. By serving as the venue for his festivals, Munich would, he said, endow the rest of Germany with a cultural legacy that might lend all Germans a stronger sense of national identity.

But complications soon arose which thwarted this ambition. Wagner's scandalous love affair with Cosima von Bülow, his luxurious living at public expense, and his repeated interference in state politics, quickly alienated the people of Munich. The press complained that Wagner and his followers were "thrusting themselves between us Bavarians and our beloved king" (Blunt, 1970, p. 40). People compared

Wagner to Lola Montez, the self-styled "Spanish dancer" who stole the heart (and some of the treasure) of Ludwig's grandfather, Ludwig I. Ludwig's prime minister told the king that he had to choose "between the love and esteem of your loyal subjects and the 'friendship' of Richard Wagner" (Blunt, 1970, p. 67).

So smitten was he with Wagner that Ludwig contemplated abdicating rather than sending his friend away, but Wagner talked him out of this rash step: a Ludwig without power would be useless to him. So Wagner himself left Munich, which he now denounced as a place where baptized Jews, won over by the Jesuits, instructed the people and their king. And in Triebschen near Lucerne, where he lived in exile at Ludwig's personal expense, he revived his ideal of a theater in some small German town, far from the corruption, intrigue, and decadence of the larger cities. The German spirit, he now maintained, resided primarily in the countryside; thus it was only in a village or small town where his work could be truly understood and appreciated.

The Bavarian people's resentment of Wagner was aggravated by the fact that their state faced a major political crisis in the mid-1860s, namely, the pressing dilemma of how to respond to the struggle between Austria and Prussia for control over the emerging national state of Germany. Having recently fallen under the influence of a federalist thinker named Constantine Frantz, Wagner took the view that Bavaria should not align itself with either Austria or Prussia, but maintain its own independent line. He insisted that Germany must not be dominated either by Austria, which he said was run by the Jesuits, or by Prussia, which he insisted was as alien to the German spirit as international Jewry, and which was governed by "barbarian Junkers" like Otto von Bismarck, Prussia's prime minister. "The German will enjoy what is advantageous to him only when Bismarck and similar poor imitations of the most ungermanic spirit are completely finished," Wagner wrote (Millington, 1987, p. 81). Assuring Ludwig that he was "royalist through and through," Wagner advised the king that "only the German princes can save Germany" (Millington, 1988, p. 680); and he recommended that Ludwig immediately seek the counsel of Constantine Frantz, who, he confided to the king, had recently written "to tell me that the harmonies of my music had revealed to him a picture of Germany's future" (Millington, 1988, p. 681).

Clearly Wagner hoped through Ludwig and Frantz to shape the course of German history; and characteristically, he coupled Germany's fate with the success of his own artistic endeavors. As he wrote Frantz:

The fact that, through my art, I am in a position here to render a king lucid and fully clairvoyant who is otherwise incapable of properly appreciating the most everyday aspects of real life; that I may hope to persuade this same king to embrace the grandest and most far-reaching resolves and actions because of his inspired love for me—this must fill me, in my exalted mood, with a well-nigh momentous presentiment of the spirit and manner in which I might yet be called upon to influence Germany itself. I am too experienced to indulge in any vain and cosy self-deception in this matter. This much, however, is now clear to me; my own artistic ideal stands or falls with the salvation of Germany; without Germany's greatness my art was wholly a dream: if this dream is to find fulfillment, Germany, too, must necessarily attain to her preordained greatness [Millington, 1988 pp. 685–686].

Two months before the outbreak of the Austro-Prussian war of 1866, Wagner tried to convince Ludwig to mediate between the two states so as to foil the aggressive plans of Bismarck, that "ambitious Junker" who was betraying "his imbecile of a King," William I of Prussia (Millington, 1988, p. 691). He warned that a war would lead to "mass chaos" and the destruction of Germany. He asked Ludwig:

To what avail shall my life have been then, to what avail my work and my creativity? To what avail the godlike love of my dear redeemer, who has rescued me and my works for the world? My artistic ideal stands and falls with Germany, just as my works live or die with her. What will follow the downfall of the German princes is that Jewish-Germanic mass which I once described to you, in my diary: You know what I mean by the word "German" [Millington, 1988, pp. 691–692].

Whether or not Ludwig understood Wagner's conception of the word *German*—and he could be forgiven for not doing so since it changed so often—the king could not stand aside when Austria and Prussia went to war in the summer of 1866. Bavaria sided with Austria in the conflict, a decision Wagner regretted, though he preferred it to an alliance with Prussia. Yet as soon as the war turned decisively in Prussia's favor, which it very quickly did, Wagner advised Ludwig to renounce the Austrians and "purge the Jesuits" from his cabinet (Westernhagen, 1943, p. 46). To his old friend August Röckel he wrote: "My friend! If you want to and must pursue politics, then adhere to Bismarck and Prussia. I know no other way"(Millington, 1987, p. 82). King Ludwig, alas, ignored the Master's advice to abandon Austria, and Bavaria went down to defeat with its Catholic ally.

It took Wagner only one month after Prussia's victory to begin publicly celebrating Bismarck as the new savior of Germany, and Prussia as the wave of the German future. It seemed that for Wagner, Prussia after all embodied the true German spirit, though of course this would be more clearly evident if it embraced Wagner's "Germanic Art."

Prussia's rapid ascendancy was indeed one of the factors that induced Wagner to think of the small Franconian town of Bayreuth as a possible home for the festival theater he still dreamed of establishing. Bayreuth, it is true, lay in Bavarian territory, which was advantageous for Wagner since he hoped to continue to tap Ludwig for financial support. But Bayreuth (like Nuremberg, which he also considered) was both part of Ludwig's territory *and* a former Prussian seat. In the eighteenth century it had been the residence of Margravin Wilhelmine, Friedrich the Great's favorite sister. It was she, in fact, who had built the local opera house which Wagner initially thought might serve as a suitable stage for his music-dramas, but which on closer inspection turned out to be much too small. At any rate, a move to Bayreuth might connote his staking a claim to the Prussian-backed German nationalist movement, and perhaps even to the largesse of the ascendant Hohenzollern House. Moreover, Bayreuth, unlike Nuremberg, had no ongoing theatrical operation of its own which might have competed with Wagner's enterprise. Indeed, it had no prominent cultural or social institutions of any kind, save perhaps for the local lunatic asylum, which some Wagner detractors would eventually consider a haven of sanity in comparison to the Festspielhaus. Bayreuth, in other words, was a place where Wagner could be king, a place he could put on the map as the new capital of German art. It might become, as he put it, "a sort of Art-Washington D.C." (Karbaum, 1976, p. 29).

As a step toward realizing this ideal, Wagner considered writing Bismarck's wife in 1869 to ask her to encourage her husband to step forward as a patron of the festival project. Cosima persuaded him that the time was not ripe for such a move. But one year later the Franco-Prussian war broke out, and the German victories that soon culminated in national unity under Prussian hegemony confirmed Wagner in his belated admiration for things Prussian, and reinforced his conviction that his own artistic destiny lay with the new Reich. In April 1871 he wrote to a friend in Berlin that the recent unification of Germany had revived his "confidence in the future." Only now, he said, could he truly understand and admire the German spirit, adding that anyone who "did not understand figures such as Bismarck, Roon, and Moltke [generals who had orchestrated Germany's victory over France] were very much to be pitied" (Millington, 1988, p. 780). He had no pity, however, for the defeated French, whom he had never forgiven for failing adequately to recognize his genius. Calling the French "the putrefaction of the Renaissance," and Paris "this kept woman of the world," he suggested that the burning of the French capital "would be a symbol of the world's liberation at last from the pressure of all that is bad" (Aberbach, 1984, p. 151). Adolf Hitler, of course, was to harbor similar aggressive designs near the end of World War II, but his generals refused to carry out his order to destroy Paris.

Flushed with excitement over the unification of Germany through "blood and iron," and as jingoistic a German as could be found in the new Reich, Wagner began a full-blown crusade to conquer the imperial capital for his art in general, and for his theater project in particular. He began his imperial suit by dispatching patriotic poems and musical compositions to Berlin. He offered to compose the music for a "grand solemnity" honoring the victorious German troops. In April 1871 he embarked on a fund raising tour that focused on the imperial capital, despite warnings from Cosima (April 15, 1871) that he "might be murdered by Berlin Jews" (C. Wagner, 1976, pp. 377–378). He managed a private audience with Bismarck, whom he sought to flatter by suggesting that the Iron Chancellor had achieved in the realm of politics what he, Wagner, had achieved in art. After their brief visit, during which Bismarck remained friendly but noncommittal, Wagner sent the chancellor a copy of his *Deutsche Kunst und deutsche Politik*, a ponderous tract which pointed up the crying need for a German national art; as well as a brochure on Bayreuth, which noted the lamentable fact that the new Reich's political successes had not managed to turn the German people away from foreign art and toward the geniuses of their own country. In 1874, still without any positive response from Bismarck, Wagner sought in vain to approach the emperor through emissaries with an offer of the premiere performance of the complete *Ring* cycle, which he hoped to stage in the following year "as a quinquennial celebration to mark the victory over France in 1871" (Millington, 1988, p. 826). A year later, having had to postpone the premiere due to lack of adequate funding, he wrote the emperor directly, asking for a grant from his special fund for furthering "worthy national interests"(Kerr, 1912, p. 238).

The emperor promised a modest contribution of 30,000 thalers, but Bismarck, who thus far had ignored Wagner's entreaties, canceled the grant and suggested that the matter be taken up by the Reichstag. When he learned of this Wagner exploded in indignation. What an impertinence to suggest that *he*, Germany's greatest living composer, should have to grovel in the dust before a "pack of mediocrities" who had not "the slightest appreciation of [his] work!" (January 14, 1876, C. Wagner, 1976, pp. 964–965). This was a very revealing statement: it seemed that Wagner now believed that his *Ring* could be understood by conservative generals like Roon and Moltke, but not by the parliamentarians who represented what was left of the liberal-democratic ideal in Germany. One is tempted to say that he had come a long way from 1848, and in some senses he had, but one should also recall that he had always been something of a closet monarchist and had never trusted the artistic instincts of the German masses. In rejecting any association with the Reichstag, and in trying to deal only on a personal level with the great men of the empire, Wagner was showing his true political colors and belying his self-proclaimed status as artistic tribune of the German people.

Blaming Bismarck for the failure of his imperial suit, Wagner now turned his full wrath upon the man he had so recently glorified. He called the chancellor a *Sauhetzer* (pig caller), and said that he had shown himself to be a coward, failing to support the Bayreuth enterprise because he feared the opprobium of the Berlin Jewish press (Large and Weber, 1984, p. 75).

The real reasons for Bismarck's rebuff of Wagner were, as one might imagine, rather different. Having just engineered a convincing victory over France, Bismarck had no desire to rub salt in Gallic wounds by associating the new German empire too closely with Wagner, who had become embarrassingly strident in his Francophobia. The chancellor also understood that King Ludwig of Bavaria, who was still quite gaga over Wagner despite the latter's blatant exploitation of his generosity and love, would be offended if he thought that Bismarck and the emperor were (as Bismarck put it) "poaching on his private hunting reserve" (Westernhagen, 1943, p. 61). It was important not to alienate Ludwig because Bavaria's support was necessary to lend cohesion to the new empire. Thus Wagner's crusade to win imperial backing for his Bayreuth venture fell victim to the complexities of Bismarckian politics—complexities which a self-obsessed megalomaniac like Wagner could not have been expected to understand or appreciate. "Wagner," complained Bismarck after their meeting in 1871, "always has to be first. I'm too busy for such silliness" (Westernhagen, 1943, p. 61).

Given this attitude of the chancellor's, it is not surprising that Bismarck stayed away from the first Bayreuth Festival in 1876, as did the celebrated generals Roon and Moltke. The emperor consented to put in an appearance, but he left early to attend a military maneuver. Wagner was thus forced to recognize that he had failed to make his Bayreuth Festival the "artistic sister" of German unification, the theatrical symbol of Germany's national consciousness and ascendant military power (Large, 1978, p. 162).

He had also failed, one should add, to realize his earlier dream of creating a popular festival for the serious but impecunious devotees of his work. His inability to cover the full costs of *The Ring* production either through subsidies from Ludwig or the sale of subscriptions to members of the various Richard Wagner societies around the world meant that he had to charge high admission prices, which in turn ensured that attending the festival was to be just another pastime for the privileged, rather than the communal experience of enlightened souls he originally envisaged. In this respect the first festival established a pattern that was to persist throughout Bayreuth's history, with the exception of the performances during World War II, when the Festspielhaus was filled with wounded soldiers brought there by the Nazi government's "Strength Through Joy" program (no doubt many of the soldiers found this a particularly sadistic form of R & R).

Like his ardent disciple Adolf Hitler in the closing days of the Third Reich, Wagner in the aftermath of the first Bayreuth Festival came to believe that the German people were not worthy of him. After all, they were allowing Bismarck, that "uncouth Junker," to cast the new nation in his own image, with the result that the Reich possessed plenty of military power, but no "spirit" (Large, 1978, p. 171). In his growing disillusionment with the Fatherland, Wagner even contemplated emigrating to Minnesota, whose German-American citizens had offered to subsidize a New World Festspielhaus in Minneapolis. Quite characteristically, Wagner sought to justify this brief temptation by claiming that the purest Germanic stock was now to be found in the American Middle

West—a notion which, however, his friend Count Gobineau soon persuaded him to abandon.

I would like to conclude with just a few brief comments about Bayreuth's relationship to German nationalism in the century since Wagner's death in 1883. Like Wagner's perspective on German identity, this is a complicated story. By the end of the nineteenth century the Bayreuth Festival, now under the authoritarian control of Wagner's widow Cosima, had become fully accepted, though still not subsidized, by the political leadership of the German Empire. Emperor William II liked to think that he was a Wagnerian: he tuned his automobile horn to Wotan's leitmotif, personally designed a hideous Wagner monument (fortunately never built), and put in occasional appearances at Bayreuth. Wagner's art become so much part of the cultural mainstream in Wilhelmian Germany that it was even exploited in advertising. The Berlin popular press, for example, carried advertisements for Liebig's Meat Extract that were adorned with scenes from Wagner's music-dramas. (No doubt Wagner, a passionate vegetarian, would not have welcomed this particular sign of popular acceptance.)

More significantly, Bayreuth became a pilgrimage site for German nationalists from all parts of the Reich. They flocked there not just because they loved Wagner's music, but also because they saw the annual festivals as a potent patriotic symbol that might lend a greater sense of unity or cohesion to a nation that was still sharply divided along regional, religious, and class lines. The new Germany, moreover, lacked other convincing national symbols; it did not have a flag until 1892, or a national hymn until after World War I. By becoming a central shrine in German self-worship, the Bayreuth Festival filled this gap, at least to some degree.

Yet the festivals could not serve as an unambiguous symbol of German nationalism, because they also catered to the international Wagner movement, indeed were increasingly dependent for their financial survival on visitors from abroad. Thus Wagner's heirs, first Cosima, then his son Siegfried and daughter-in-law Winifred, were obliged to play down Bayreuth's nationalistic dimensions in order not to alienate the foreign guests. A good example of such strategic reticence occurred at the festival in 1924, when a group of Nazis jumped up at the end of *Die Meistersinger* and sang *Deutschland über Alles*. Siegfried, though (along with his wife) an early backer of Hitler, ran out on the stage and told them to desist. "Hier gilt's der Kunst!" ("Our aim is art"), he admonished (Mayer, 1976, p. 104). Clearly Siegfried suffered from the delusion that art and politics could be conveniently separated in the charged atmosphere of Weimar Germany—an endeavor that was particularly futile in a place like Bayreuth, where the distinction had always been blurred.

Separating Wagner's art from extreme nationalist politics was of course not a problem after Hitler came to power in 1933; indeed, it was not even attempted. During the Third Reich, the Festspielhaus became for the first and only time in its history a true national theater (though, as a continuing sop to an ever-smaller international clientele, never officially designated Reichsfestspielhaus). The festivals were now heavily subsidized by the government and increasingly a place of cultural worship for xenophobic Germans who took delight in having these sacred occasions more exclusively to themselves.

Had Wagner been alive to experience these developments, he might well have welcomed the state subsidies and nationalist fervor, but one would like to think that he would not have seen Nazi Bayreuth as the true fulfillment of his dream of a national theater. It is hard to believe that he would have seen the sleeping soldiers and Party bosses at Winifred's festivals as true connoisseurs of his art. And it is hard to believe that he would have welcomed the narrow provincialism and attendant artistic mediocrity that now prevailed on his beloved "Green Hill."

The festivals that have been held in Bayreuth since the Festspielhaus reopened in 1951 have in some ways been closer to the original Wagnerian ideal in that they have often been innovative and experimental. One thinks above all of Patrice Chereau's centennial *Ring*, in which the saga of the Nibelungen was presented as an allegory of the nineteenth century, with Wotan an authoritarian aristocrat of 1848, Siegfried and Brünnhilde members of the revolutionary intelligentsia, the Rhine maidens exploited whores, and the Rhine itself a polluted industrial sewer. But Wagner's ideal of a *national* theater has not been evident in post-World War II Bayreuth. The festival administration has rigorously avoided tying the enterprise to any expression of German national sentiment, catering instead to an international community of Wagnerian Frequent Flyers.

No doubt this was only appropriate in a country like Germany, where, at least until reunification, nationalism was downplayed in the interest of integrating the Federal Republic firmly into the democratic West. The new Germany of today, however, is again searching for myths and symbols to animate its revived sense of national consciousness. Wagner is enjoying a great boom in the newly unified nation. It will be interesting to observe the role that Wagner's work and the Bayreuth festivals continue to play in this latest version of the old German quest for a cohesive national identity.

REFERENCES

Aberbach, A. D. (1984), *The Ideas of Richard Wagner*. Lanham, MD: University Press of America.

Altmann, W., Ed. (1927a), *Letters of Richard Wagner*, Vol. 1. New York: Dutton.

―――― (1927b), *Letters of Richard Wagner*, Vol. 2. New York: Dutton.

Barth, H. (1975), *Wagner: A Documentary Study*. New York: Oxford University Press.

Blunt, W. (1970), *The Dream King: Ludwig II of Bavaria*. New York: Viking.

Karbaum, M. (1976), *Studien zur Geschichte der bayreuther Festspiele, 1876–1976*. Regensburg, Germany: Bosse Verlag.

Kerr, C. V., Ed. (1912), *The Bayreuth Letters of Richard Wagner*. Boston: Small Maynard.

Large, D. C. (1978), The political background of the foundation of the Bayreuth festival, 1876. *Central European Hist.*, 11:162–172.

―――― Weber, W., Eds. (1984), *Wagnerism in European Culture and Politics*. Ithaca, NY: Cornell University Press.

Mayer, H. (1976), *Richard Wagner in Bayreuth*. New York: Rizzoli.

Millington, B. (1987), *Wagner*. New York: Vintage.

―――― Ed. (1988), *Selected Letters of Richard Wagner*. New York: W. W. Norton.

Wagner, C. (1976), *Die Tagebücher*, Vol. 1. Munich, Germany: Piper Verlag.

Wagner, R. (1911), *Sämptliche Schriften und Dichtungen*, 5th ed., 12 vols. Leipzig: Breitkopf und Härtel.

―――― (1973), *Wagner Writes from Paris. Stories, Essays, and Articles by the Young Composer*, ed. R. L. Jacobs & G. Skelton. London: Allen & Unwin.

―――― (1980), *The Diary of Richard Wagner 1865–1882: The Brown Book*, tr. G. Bird. London: Cambridge University Press.

Westernhagen, C. von (1943), Wagner und das Reich. In: *Schriften der Richard Wagner Forschungsstätte*, ed. O. Strobel. Karlsruhe, Germany: Verlag G. Braun.

Windell, G. C. (1976), Hegel, Feuerbach, and Wagner's *Ring*. *Central European Hist.*, 9:25–57.

5

Notes on Incest Themes in Wagner's *Ring* Cycle

George H. Pollock, M.D., Ph.D.

Prolific composer of massive operatic works, librettist, essayist, a political activist who spent many years in exile as a result of his activities, Wagner wrote extensively on drama, philosophy, opera, music, art, and politics. If Wagner was a controversial figure in his own lifetime, he remains so today because of the major role his music played during the Third Reich. This came about not only because of Wagner's own virulent anti-Semitism and his son Siegfried's support of the Nazis (he was director of the opera house at Bayreuth and a prolific though minor composer), but because Hitler saw Wagner's operas in general, and the great *Ring* cycle in particular, with its use of Norse legends, its tales of gods and heroes, as fitting "theme music" for the fantasied Thousand Year Reich. (One wonders what the Nazis were doing during performances of *Götter-dämmerung*. Had they truly understood Wagner's ideas, they would have predicted the fiery end of the Third Reich. There was not to be an eternal fatherland populated by gods who control all, but instead, there would be a final curtain call with applause for the death of tyranny.) At any rate, Wagner's musical genius is such that today his work has come to be considered on its own merits as an essential part of the repertoire. Magee (1968), for example, believes that the deciding factor in the

Reprinted, with permission, from *Psychoanalytic Explorations in Music, Second Series*, ed. S. Feder, R. L. Karmel, and G. H. Pollock. Madison, CT: International Universities Press, 1993, pp. 195–216.

survival and popularity of a particular opera is the music alone. Certainly, one cannot dismiss a pivotal figure such as Wagner because of his biases and prejudices, without first considering what he had to say and create. Goldman and Sprinchorn (1964) note that "perhaps no artist in the history of Western art, has ever had so much to say about his own life, works, and ideas as did Richard Wagner" (p. 11). On the other side of the coin, Goldman and Sprinchorn point out that over ten thousand articles about Wagner's life and work have appeared over the past hundred years. Much has been written about Wagner's views on politics, revolution, philosophy, myths and their derivation, his anti-Semitism, his relationship to Nietzsche, vegetarianism, and his innumerable affairs with his closest friends' wives. But, as Magee also notes, were it not for Wagner's music, none of this would be of much interest.

Wagner himself knew that his music played a key role in "Bringing what had been unconscious to consciousness" (Magee, 1968, p. 80). This is the essential element that makes Wagner's ideas of interest in the context of this volume.

The focus of this essay will be on Wagner's life course as expressed in the *Ring* operas, with the attendant themes of incest, aging, immortality, and death. The discussion will be a discursive one in which the basic biographical facts of Wagner's life may, as it were, be read against the recurring themes that run throughout his body of work, most especially, of course, *The Ring*.

Wagner's parents were Carl Friedrich and Johanna Rosina Wagner; Richard was their ninth child (Millington, 1987). Carl was an amateur actor and costume designer. Both he and his wife Johanna had numerous extramarital affairs—Johanna, for example, was not, as she claimed, the illegitimate daughter of Prince Constantine of Saxe-Weimar-Eisenach, but his mistress. Thus, there is a question of whether Ludwig Geyer, an actor-painter-playwright friend of Carl's, slept with Johanna while her husband was alive. Certainly, Geyer was a close friend of both Wagners, and Johanna took the infant Richard to see Geyer, having to cross one hundred miles of enemy occupied territory to do so (this was in 1813 at the time of the Napoleonic Wars). Millington suggests "that Johanna urgently wished to show the baby to its father" (1987, p. 2). Carl Friedrich Wagner died on November 23, 1813, when Richard was 6 months old, and Geyer immediately took over the family. Johanna and Geyer were married on August 28, 1814, six months before the birth of their daughter, Cäcilie, of whom Richard was later to become particularly fond. Geyer was a good father to his large family, and he insisted that Richard be sent to an excellent boarding school. But when Geyer's health became precarious because of tuberculosis and he could no longer work, Richard returned home. Johanna would ask the boy to play the piano for his sick stepfather, and Geyer is known to have remarked on the boy's talent. Richard was 8 years old when Geyer died. No firm conclusions can be reached about Richard's paternity, but in practical terms, Geyer was the only father Richard knew. We must also assume, however, that there remained the distant but powerful image in the unconscious of Richard Wagner, of Carl Friedrich Wagner who had vanished so early, but whose existence inevitably would have continued to resonate throughout his son's life.

Richard was described as an abnormally sensitive and imaginative boy who suffered from nightmares. "Each night he would startle the household by wakening out of ghostly dreams and screaming" (Watson, 1979, p. 25). Loneliness had a special terror for him, and he continued to have grotesque nightmares all his life. The death of Carl Friedrich when Richard was 6 months old, and the death of his 5-year-old sister six months later, at a time when Johanna their mother was involved with Geyer and pregnant with his child, must have brought an atmosphere of anguish and turmoil to the household, and doubtless contributed to Richard's night terrors.

Wagner's abilities, which played so important a role in his later creative life, surfaced early. At the age of 4, he made his only appearance as an actor, in Schiller's *Wilhelm Tell.* (Both Wagner's father, an amateur actor, and particularly Geyer, who in addition to his other abilities had occasional roles in the Dresden Opera company formed by the composer Carl-Maria von Weber, may be assumed to have been influential in Wagner's early development of artistic abilities—it was, as it were, in the air he breathed in childhood.) Not only was there the piano playing that Geyer had remarked upon, but also compositions; in 1820, Richard wrote two overtures; he was 7 years of age.

Richard was strongly influenced by the world of E. T. A. Hoffmann, his musical criticism, and tales. Wagner's first opera, *The Wedding*, had occult themes related to Hoffmann's writings. Wagner destroyed the libretto of this work, leaving only the music for the opening scene and a synopsis of the plot. It is worth recounting the bare bones of the plot because the themes of love and death that were to run through all of Wagner's operas are present here in this very early work. Codolt, a family enemy, sets his sights on Ada, who is marrying another. On the wedding night, he forces his way into her chamber where she awaits her new husband. She struggles with him, and with superhuman strength throws him out of the tower window through which he entered. He falls to his death. Revenge is demanded, but the bride's father averts this by saying that God's judgment will fall on the murderer at the time of Codolt's funeral. Ada comes to the funeral, and when she sees Codolt's corpse, she sinks lifeless upon the body. This first opera ends like so many of Wagner's later operas, with the death of both the leading male and female characters. The oedipal themes of the "outsider" trying to force his way into a marital relationship were to be repeated in many of Wagner's later works (Codolt's death plunge from the phallic tower after being expelled through a window by Ada might be seen as a highly compressed birth scene combined with punishment for oedipal wishes).

It is my belief that this thematic repetition and perseveration tells us not only of Wagner's lifelong preoccupation with death as the reward for incest, but foretells the fate that is presented in the final opera of *The Ring, Götterdämmerung.* Here, it is not only the individual, but the whole social order that is plunged into the abyss. Reflected here also is the typical ending that Wagner derived from his study of Sophocles' Oedipus trilogy, where both female and male characters perish in the finale, leaving no survivors. In other words, for the participants it is truly the end of the world, for when they die nothing of them remains. The murder of Laius leads inexorably to the marriage of Oedipus and Jocasta, and after this is revealed, to the destruction of Thebes itself. The actions of individuals bring down society.

Even though Wagner never mastered classical Greek, his love for Greek culture and legends began at age 8 in 1821 when he heard about the Greek war of independence. The Greeks were fighting for their freedom after 400 years of Turkish rule. The Greek language was kept alive throughout that period by the Greek Orthodox priests who taught it secretly in mountain hideaways. This preservation of the language enabled the society to remain cohesive long enough to rise up and fight the oppressor. It was a war with enormous romantic appeal, which indeed attracted such people as the romantic poet Byron. Richard's fascination with Greek mythology and history, we may surmise, was reinforced by the stories of this real life struggle for freedom. This may not only have led him into Greek culture, to the Oedipus of Sophocles, and to Aeschylus and his Oresteia plays (see Ewans [1982] for a comparison of Wagner and Aeschylus and *The Ring* and the Oresteia), but also influenced in some measure his later political involvements. I have studied thematic perseveration in other musicians and artists (Pollock, 1982, 1989) and believe that the creator's basic themes get reworked and elaborated and the thread can be identified and then correlated with biographical details.

As we have seen, Wagner's early life included the deaths of his father, sister, and the man who was truly his father, Geyer, when Richard was 8 years old. At 14, when he was writing his first major dramatic work, Richard, having used Geyer's name throughout his childhood, again took his father's name, Wagner. Thus, we see a clear connection between loss, death, and creativity in Wagner's life. The first major work, taking place in adolescence, causes Wagner effectively to resurrect the dead father by taking his last name. In doing so he simultaneously acknowledges his loss whilst affirming the powerful and essential connection with Carl Friedrich Wagner. It may also have been a way of distancing himself from the oedipal issues that he would have been reworking at that age. By attaching himself to the mythological father, whom he knew only by repute, he could contain and minimize the dangerous feelings of oedipal triumph resulting from Geyer's death when the boy was 8 years old. At the same time, it is noteworthy that throughout his life, Wagner was accustomed to wear the painter's smock that was Geyer's preferred garb.

Had he not been a composer, Wagner would have been significant as an essayist and thinker. He wrote his principal prose essays between the years 1848 and 1851, a period of profound turmoil for him, with both internal and external crises. From 1847 to 1853, when he began *The Ring*, he wrote no music. Goldman and Sprinchorn mention that during this time, Wagner wrote "a series of theoretical treatises designed to explain the nature of his projected artwork and the circumstances, political, cultural, and artistic, which made its realization necessary" (p. 13). This may perhaps be viewed less as a period when he "couldn't write any music" and more as one of intellectual reorganization. This was also the period when he was active politically. He was involved in the May 1849 Dresden Revolution, as a result of which he had to flee Germany. He settled in Zurich where he lived until 1859, and it was there that he composed two-thirds of *The Ring* and began *Tristan.* In later years, when Wagner no longer wrote formal essays, he still addressed intellectual and philosophical topics in his many letters and had many conversations about these topics with his friends. In his thinking, Wagner was both original and derivative. He was stimulated by the ideas of others, he could integrate them into his own thoughts, he could formulate what he experienced at a very deep level, and he was very resourceful and versatile.

His use of myths and legends as the basis of his work was part of a major cultural trend in his day. The Brothers Grimm, collectors of folktales, had been members of the Göttingen seven, a group of university professors who had protested against despotism in 1837, and their work must surely have been familiar to Wagner. As Michaelis-Jena (1970) notes: "[T]he Romantics. . . . saw folk literature as a product of natural evolution, distinct from the deliberate culture of their age, an expression of wisdom and fundamental truth . . . " (p. 5). The Grimms, however, saw folktales "as the debris of myths, primeval beliefs, religion, early customs and law. . . . ancestral reminiscences to be collected for the investigation of ancient German literature, and to be treated with respect" (p. 5). It was perhaps this latter view of folktales and myth that was closest to Wagner's own. It may have been this grasping for historical facts amongst myths and legends that has caused some commentators to accuse him of a kind of fake historicity. In his "making the unconscious conscious," the attention he paid to dreams and the "dreamlike" condensations of myth, and their role in his creative life as a composer, he broke new ground.

As we have seen, Wagner had acquired accomplishments at an early age, playing the piano and writing music. Throughout his life he was notable for his all-round ability in every aspect of the staging of operatic works. He wrote the librettos as well as the music, had a hand in the design of costumes and scenery, and all the other innumerable technicalities involved in presenting an opera. In this we may see, perhaps, in addition to Wagner's innate abilities, the influence of the multitalented father, Geyer.

There are many frames of reference one can use in approaching Wagner: there were his operas, there was his place in the music of his time, there were myth and legend, philosophy, and the historical currents of the period and the effects they had upon his ideas and creativity.

For example, George Bernard Shaw (1911) saw *The Ring* as a sociopolitical drama. Alberich, the dwarf, renounces love and beauty for gold and power. Others have seen *The Ring* as a reenactment of the ancient Greek drama of Oedipus; still others understand the cycle as a religious statement. Alternatively, it might be seen as symbolically portraying the life course: birth, growth and development, decline, death. There are those who would see *The Ring* as Wagner's autobiography. And indeed, we can perhaps only fully understand *The Ring* by considering each and every one of these aspects.

First, however, let us take a look at Wagner the man. Wagner's affairs with his friends' wives were legendary, yet paradoxically, Hans von Bülow, with whose wife Wagner had three illegitimate children and later married, spoke of " 'this glorious, unique man whom one must venerate like a god' " (Wagner, quoted in Magee, 1968, p. 32). Wagner's affairs, which were well known even during his marriages, did not appear to interfere at all with his creativity. Similarly, his revolutionary-political activities, the fact that he lived in exile for a period of time, and his fiscal problems, did not diminish his creativity, even though they did cause him some passing anguish. External traumas, which would otherwise demolish less "strong" individuals, seemingly did not impair Wagner's creativity—instead, they may even have contributed to it.

There were objections to Wagner's use of the incest theme in his own day. He dealt openly with incest on stage, and many people continue to be especially disturbed by the passionate love scenes between brother and sister which culminate in sexual intercourse and pregnancy. For example, in the second act of *Die Walküre*, where Wotan says:

> What wrong
> Did these two do
> When spring united them in love?

And when Fricka (goddess of marriage) cries out:

> My heart shudders,
> my brain reels;
> Marital intercourse
> Between brother and sister!

When did anyone live to see it:
Brother and sister *physically* lovers?

Wotan replies:

You have lived to see it today.
Learn from this
That things can ordain themselves
Though they never happened before.
That these two love each other
Is obvious to you.

Listen to some honest advice:
Smile on their love, and bless
Siegmund and Sieglinde's union.
Their sweet joy
Will reward you for your blessing [Magee, 1968, p. 35].

And then Wotan, speaking for Wagner, says:

You want to understand always,
Only what you are used to:
My mind is reaching out towards
Things that have never happened [Magee, 1968, p. 35].

Oedipal sexuality is an important theme in both *Siegfried* and *Parsifal*, as Magee notes (p. 36). Wagner anticipated Freud's observations in many ways, for example, libido theory, repression, the Oedipus complex, guilt, and punishment. Magee refers to the fact that the operas of Wagner's artistic maturity are "like animated textbooks of psychoanalysis" (p. 36). Wagner had referred to music bringing the unconscious to consciousness and in this he captures, too, the essence of psychoanalytic thought. Ideas that are otherwise unexpressed and unknown in consciousness can be expressed in music, in which the essence of the emotions are represented in sound. Fifty years later Freud was to develop a scientific method of describing the functioning of the psyche through his clinical and theoretical formulations, not only regarding the Oedipus complex but in his writings about the unconscious and the repressed—the essential source of all art.

As Wagner had done, Freud turned to the plays of Sophocles for inspiration and instruction. In Wagner's works one finds the forbidden (such as incest) expressed openly, and the consciousness of performers and audience alike reverberates to its direct, clear presentation. I believe, as do others, that what Wagner produced stems thematically from what he perceived within himself and perhaps what he acted upon. Had he been involved in an incestuous relationship with one or more of his sisters? He is said to have been particularly close to Cäcilie, his younger sister/stepsister, and to Rosalie. (As has been noted elsewhere, incestuous feelings for the parent are frequently expressed with a sibling, where the relationship is more manageable than it would be with a parent.) Whether or not there was a physical relationship between Wagner and one or more of his sisters is beside the point. What is significant is Wagner's ability to go straight to the sources within him and tap them in the service of his art. That he could take the reality of those overwhelming feelings and use their reality as the organizing theme in a series of works of art is undoubtedly true.

Wagner's impact on the society and culture of his time was extraordinary. His audiences were faced with the darkest, the most powerful, the most essential themes of human existence, and such was the power of Wagner's music, that it was impossible for listeners to see his operatic works as mere entertainments outside their own existence. Willy nilly, they, like audiences today, were drawn into the dramas of incest, love, murder, rape. They could see themselves as the flawed heroes and heroines, struggling with their impulses in a world they could not control, be forced to confront themselves as the Alberichs of this world, hungry for the power that comes with gold. They could see themselves as Siegfrieds and Sieglindes acting upon their feelings despite taboos against their expression. Wagner made his audiences confront their own mortality, their own frailty, the melding of power and helplessness in the face of the cosmos that lies at the center of human experience. As Magee (1968) notes: "Some were overwhelmed, and worshipped. Others regarded his almost incredible lack of restraint as shocking or frightening, or mad, or immoral, or in some other way deeply disturbing" (p. 40).

Wagner's idealization of the Greek theater was based on his ideas of what constitutes great art: "a religious occasion, the participation of the entire community, and the cooperation of all the arts in the dramatic representation of a mythic action" (Goldman and Sprinchorn, 1964,

p. 19). Commenting on creativity, Wagner likened the birth of music to the birth of a child in all its cosmic power: "By virtue of its nature and origin, then, music carries an almost unbearable weight of meaning" (Wagner, cited in Rather, 1979, p. 138).

In his operatic works, Wagner focused on legends that were tragic in outcome and where suffering and death, and the total destruction of the protagonists' world, as in the story of Oedipus, are the major themes. Oedipus, the tragic hero, struggles, survives, kills, mutilates, and ultimately the line he created is destroyed (Pollock, 1986).

Despite, or perhaps because of, his intense relationship with dreams and the dreamlike condensations of myths and legends, Wagner could write, when he was in the midst of his most passionate romance, "I have at last found a quietus that in wakeful nights helps me to sleep. This is the genuine, ardent longing for death, for absolute unconsciousness, total non-existence. Freedom from all dreams is our only final salvation" (Wagner [1856], as cited in Goldman and Sprinchorn [1964, p. 27]).

There is a duality in all of human experience, between life and death, love and hate. But it seems particularly marked in Wagner, this larger than life figure, passionate in love and revolution, a man who truly lived in the world, and yet, as the quotation suggests, simultaneously longed for intrauterine oblivion.

We see and hear this in *Tristan and Isolde,* which is filled with the dualism of love (life) and death, love and hate, and I believe we can see these elements most clearly in *The Ring* and its underlying oedipal theme.

Wagner believed that Greek culture, with its roots in religion, and its direct expression of religious feeling through the drama, in which poetry, music, dance, song, were brought together to celebrate the glory and truth of existence, and with its roots firmly set in the Greek religion, reached its high point in Greek tragedy. This was a drama in which the whole community participated. Wagner like Freud believed that with the fragmentation of the arts and religion human beings came to look on their bodies and feelings with shame, suspicion, fear and guilt—especially in terms of instinctual love. Life became a burden, filled with sin and rewarded at death by an existence of eternal bliss. Wagner felt that these religious beliefs, which had developed after the heyday of Greek classical culture, were anti-art. Man was alienated from his own nature, especially his emotions, and had the feeling that he was a "guilty worm."

Rightly or wrongly, Wagner felt that religion had come to be based on the celebration of death rather than life, and that inevitably this was hostile to the expression of spirituality.

The decline of the theater from the Greek pinnacle of religious experience to one where people came to be entertained with frivolity and emptiness, appeared to Wagner to be vulgar, socially exclusive, grotesque, and fragmented. He forbade the customary ballet to be performed before his operas began. Aside from being light entertainment to, as it were, warm up the audience, the ballet presumably allowed latecomers to be seated. Wagner wanted to return to the older, more meaningful Greek ideal where all the elements of the arts were unified in an enactment that was in essence religious. In addition to social and political dimensions, he was concerned with music-drama that expressed inner emotions and not just the outer motives that carry the plot. Myth was the ideal—ageless in that it could reach beyond time and place and deal with the core of universal truths. His sense of myth as speaking direct from the psyche of humanity, his intuitive grasp of symbolism (as Magee [1968] points out, he was the "progenitor of the Symbolist Movement in French poetry") gave him the ability to unify all the elements into an artistic whole, as the Greeks had done. Drama was the means, music the end, and the participants, both performers and audience, could experience what was being communicated in a more total sense.

Wagner of all composers can only be understood by considering all aspects of his life: some regard him as politically naive, a utopian. The essence of a utopia, with its belief in the perfectibility of human institutions, laws, and social conditions, is that the human inhabitants become passive observers of laws which are agreed to be for the benefit of all. A utopia is not a place for individualists. This leads directly to Wagner's romantic idealization of ancient Greece. Central to Greek understanding of the human condition was its innate passivity. The gods were seen as controlling the lives of human beings entirely, as they fought and loved and connived on Mount Olympus. The Trojan War, for example, was understood by the Greeks as being entirely an artefact of politicking by the gods. Human beings could struggle to have control over their destiny, but they could never win against the power of the gods. This aspect of Greek thought is certainly apparent in Wagner's operas, particularly in *The Ring* cycle. Magee (1968) points out that even Wotan, the ruler of the gods, is "from the very beginning of *The Ring* at the mercy of forces he is powerless to control . . . " (pp. 14–15). He also says:

> [R]eality for Wagner is always found in the psyche, not in the external world. . . . It has been said of *The Ring* that in the deepest sense there is only one character, the different "characters" being aspects of a single personality, so that the work is a portrait of the psyche as well as a depiction of the world [Magee, 1968].

If we look at the passivity in the face of fate, along with the portrait of the inner world of the characters as aspects of the inner world of one character, we may with little difficulty conclude that we are looking into Wagner's spirit itself.

THE THEMES OF WAGNER'S OPERAS

We will now briefly outline the plots of Wagner's main operas:

1. *Rienzi* (1837–1840). The opera is filled with violence and rebellion, murder and plotting, assassination and treachery, fighting and killing. In the last act, Rienzi and his sister die together in the collapse of a burning building.

2. *The Flying Dutchman* (1840–1841). This is a music-drama rather than an opera, and it is based on Heine's version of the legend of the Flying Dutchman. The captain is condemned to sail the seas until Judgment Day unless he finds a woman who will love him faithfully until death. He finds Senta, who is loved by Eric. While she pledges her love for the Captain, Eric pleads with her to stay with him. Overhearing this and fearing he has been forsaken, the Captain flees to his ship. Senta throws herself off a cliff into the sea, the phantom ship sinks, and Senta and the Dutchman are seen rising in each other's embrace and floating upwards. Senta has sacrificed herself in order to be with the man she loves.

3. *Tannhäuser* (1842–1845). Elisabeth and Tannhäuser love one another. Elisabeth is loved by Wolfram. At the end of the opera, Tannhäuser sees her body on a bier, and sinks down on her coffin and dies.

4. *Lohengrin* (1845–1848). Again a legend of battles and killing, ending with Elsa and her brother Godfrey joined. Elsa dies in her brother's arms while her husband, Lohengrin, departs because she has betrayed him by asking him the forbidden questions about his name and birthplace. (The latter is a standard folklore motif.)

5. *Tristan and Isolde* (1854–1859). Tristan has been raised by his uncle, his parents having died while he was a baby. He slays a knight who is betrothed to Isolde, daughter of the Irish king. The wounded Tristan, keeping his identity secret, is cared for by Isolde, who is skilled in the healing arts. Isolde and Tristan fall in love, each believing their love is unrequited. Isolde decides to take a death potion; Tristan, thinking she will marry another, decides to share it with her. A love potion is substituted, and they declare their love for one another. Soon after arriving in Cornwall, Tristan is badly wounded by one of the followers of the slain knight. Tristan and Isolde die together.

6. *The Mastersingers of Nuremberg* (1845–1867). Beckmesser and Walther von Stolzing both love Eva. Hans Sachs is the kind father who helps von Stolzing in his quest for love and fulfillment with Eva—something perhaps that Wagner would have liked if he had had a father beyond his early years. Wagner may have seen himself as Walther, helped by an older man to achieve fulfilling adulthood and resolve his own oedipal competitions and conflicts. It is worth noting, that in this, the only one of Wagner's operas that is said to be based on a real life story, there is no death action.

7. *The Ring of the Nibelungs* (see below).

8. *Parsifal* (1845–1882). Here Wagner combined three legends together. This is an opera full of magic, deceptions, death, grief, the death of a former king. Kundry, the main female character, "sinks gently into the sleep of death" (Kobbé, 1919, p. 277).

9. *Leubald and Adelaide* (1827–1828). As noted earlier, this was Richard Wagner's first monumental romantic drama, begun when he was 14 years old. (He planned to set *Leubald* to music once he had learned about music theory.) Sabor (1989) notes that Wagner wrote to a friend that he remembered a dream from his youth in which he saw Shakespeare and spoke with him (p. 40). It was this fascination with Shakespeare that played an important role in Wagner's writing of *Leubald*. Wagner himself noted that the plot of the play was based loosely on Hamlet. He said: " 'The difference was that my hero, confronted with the ghost of a father murdered in similar circumstances and crying for

vengeance, is roused to such violent action that he commits a series of murders and finally becomes insane' " (Wagner [1879] quoted in Sabor [1989]). It is of interest to see how the recurring themes of violence, death, and oedipal conflicts appeared in this the very first theatrical work that Wagner wrote. Wagner himself noted that in *Leubald* he killed off so many characters that he had to bring them back as ghosts in the last acts "for want of living characters" (Mander and Mitchenson, 1977, p. 24).

Finally, to conclude this brief discussion of the operas, let us note the themes of two operas that Wagner composed very early in his career. In *The Wedding* (1832–1833), treachery and mistrust are in evidence at the wedding to which former enemies are invited. In *The Fairies* (1832–1834), the themes include the death of a father king, loss of a wife and children, magical changes, deception, choices between a mortal's death on earth or immortality in fairyland, wars and death, the underworld and the eventual reunion with the hero and his wife who become the Fairy King and Queen. This was Wagner's first completed opera, finished when he was aged 20. The reference to death is clear in the turning to stone of the key characters.

WAGNER, OEDIPUS, AND THE RING OF THE NIBELUNGS

THE RING OF THE NIBELUNGS

1. The Rheingold (1851–1854)
2. The Valkyries (1851–1856)
3. Siegfried (1851–1871)
4. The Twilight of the Gods (1848–1874)

Rank, in his magnificent 1912 monograph on *The Incest Theme in Literature and Legend* (1992), says that Wagner, by seducing other men's wives, avenged himself later in life for his mother's apparent infidelities. The winning of the sexual relationship with the wife of another and his fathering children with her (Cosima von Bülow, daughter of Franz Liszt) was an acting out of his oedipal triumph (the death of Geyer when Wagner was 8) and the consummation of the incestuous feeling toward the mother. Rank emphasized "that the incest complex plays the greatest role in the dramatic production of Richard Wagner" (1912, p. 534), and in his actual love life. His affair with Mathilda, the wife of his friend and supporter, Wesendonck, antedated his subsequent impregnations of Cosima while she was still married to von Bülow, and again represented the oedipal triumph over the father. His subsequent marriage to Cosima could be interpreted as the total possession of the mother—sexually and in all caretaking aspects. In his operas, we also frequently find the theme of the death of the father, completing what Wagner may have at first fantasied, and then in the case of father Geyer, came to pass in reality. This must indeed have been an overwhelming experience for an 8-year-old. (As noted earlier, perhaps his taking of his father's name when he was 14 was in part a way of offsetting this disturbing oedipal triumph, by connecting himself to a man he never knew.)

In *The Ring*, he also introduces sibling incest and pregnancy. Wagner was on extremely affectionate terms with his sisters, and especially with Rosalie, who died young. He apparently was not close to his brothers. In *The Valkyries* Siegmund kidnaps his beloved sister from her husband and then kills him in battle. Rank sees this as the reworking of the older and more powerful drama of killing the father and possessing the mother. Sibling incest may reflect a displacement of the oedipal drama from the parents to the sibling. *The Ring* cycle concludes with the death of Siegfried and the suicide of Brünnhilde.

Rather discusses Wagner's understanding of the Oedipus story and how it was shaped by him into the operatic tetralogy that in allegorical and symbolic fashion depicts political, social, and psychological oedipal conflict. Rather quotes Wagner referring to Sophocles' Oedipus plays as a " 'depiction of the whole history of humanity, from the origins of society to the necessary downfall of the state' " (Wagner, cited by Rather, 1979, p. xviii). Was he in this expressing a view similar to that of Marx, who saw the eventual dissolution of the state as the ideal political development?

Rather (1979) asserts that Wagner's studies of the Oedipus trilogy are essential to an understanding of *The Ring*. As a former revolutionary, friend and admirer of the anarchist Bakunin, Wagner felt that the world in which he lived was too aggressive, egoistic (narcissistic), and superficial. He anticipated Freud by fifty years when he stated that the attainment of a more ideal world required the raising to consciousness of the unconscious. Wagner also felt music was related to dreams—his operas clearly make this point. He also felt that human beings were innately self-destructive, in effect that the world would inevitably end in ruins. The breakdown of culture, values, ideals can lead to the death of society—in short, Götterdämmerung.

The song of the Nibelungs has its origins in old Nordic tales and poems dating back to the pre-Christian era of northern Europe. The medieval version of the epic dealt only with mortal men and women (Rather, 1979, p. 3). Although it uses pagan myths and traditions, it is clearly a work that comes out of a courtly Christian tradition. Wagner rewrote the story for his own dramatic purposes, also incorporating material from the pre-Christian Volsungsaga and the Icelandic Poetic Edda. This search for Nordic cultural "roots" resulted in the use of myths and legends to give a unity and a supremacy to the Nordic people—the racial myth that fueled the Nazi movement. The downfall of the gods, clearly stated in the final opera of *The Ring*, indicates Wagner's belief that lack of love, along with envy, greed, lust for gold and power are the basic causes of the ultimate disaster—death to the human race and to the land which becomes ashes; if you wish, the cremation of man.

The story of the Nibelungs was in the cultural air in Wagner's time. Several other poets and writers worked on the story (including the composer Felix Mendelssohn), but clearly Wagner made it his own. Wagner introduced several new elements to it, of which the incest motif is the most important (Rather, 1979, p. 43). In the completed *Ring*, the incest theme was given further elaboration, although several elements were either changed or eliminated from Wagner's original outline. Wotan, the chief god, condemns Siegmund to die at the hands of Hunding, Sieglinde's husband, in order to expiate his crime of incest. Sieglinde also dies and their child, Siegfried, is raised by Mime, who teaches him the smith's art. At Mime's behest, he kills the dragon guarding the hoard of gold, and hence, the source of power. Siegfried learns that Mime plans to kill him and thus possess the hoard. Siegfried kills Mime and finds the Valkyrie Brünnhilde (was this regression to the earlier mother?), who is in the forest in a deep sleep and surrounded by a ring of fire. He awakens her, and she gives him secret knowledge, warning him to be faithful and to avoid deception. Siegfried gives her the all-powerful Nibelung ring; they pledge their faith to each other and the hero departs in search of new adventures. Without going into further details of the story, we find magic, betrayal of Brünnhilde by Siegfried, the murder of Siegfried by a stab in the back, the only vulnerable point where he can be killed, the quarreling of the two half-brothers who plotted Siegfried's death, and the eventual murder of one, Gunther, by his half-brother, Hagen, who also killed Siegfried.

Brünnhilde finally returns the ring to the "sisters in the water," the Rhine maidens. She then steps into Siegfried's funeral pyre. Hagen makes one more attempt to seize the ring (genital? power?) but is drowned. After Siegfried's death, Wotan, Valhalla, and the gods are destroyed. Wotan is both father of Siegfried and Sieglinde and of Brünnhilde. "And when Siegfried first awakens Brünnhilde, he takes her to be his mother" (Rather, 1979, p. 47). In *The Ring* Wagner interpreted the elements of Sophocles' Oedipus as archaic reality. This is the thread that connects the elements of this enormous work.

Wagner, the former revolutionary, called the revolution the sublime goddess. He used the word *revolution* more than ten times in a signed article:

> I will destroy [the whole present order] for it has sprung from sin, its flower is misery and its fruit is crime. [The present order] makes millions the slaves of the few, and makes these few the slaves of their own power, their own riches. [It] makes labour a burden and an enjoyment to vice; [it compels half of mankind to perform the useless and harmful work of] soldiers, officials, speculators and money-makers . . . while the other half must support the whole edifice of shame at the cost of the exhaustion of their powers and sacrifice of all joys of life. [Down to its last trace] this insane order of things, compact of force, lies, care, hypocrisy, want, sorrow, suffering, tears, trickery and crime [must be destroyed] [Wagner, cited by Rather, 1979, pp. 47–48].

It was the downfall of society which Wagner saw as the real meaning of the Oedipus story. Incest was merely one of several instruments that led to this inevitable end. Oedipus is abandoned as a small baby because his murder of his father has been foretold. Laius exposes him on a hillside where he is found by a shepherd who takes him to the king and queen of Corinth who adopt and raise him. In Laius' desperate act, we see the beginning of the end. Jocasta was either powerless to prevent this or entirely abrogated her responsibilities toward her child. Learning from the oracle at Delphi that he will kill his father and marry his mother, Oedipus fled Corinth hoping, like his father, to avoid his fate, but at a crossroads he met and killed Laius. At Thebes he correctly answered the Sphinx's questions and won the hand of Jocasta, Laius' widow, in marriage. They had two daughters and two sons. When a plague descended on Thebes an oracle declared that the only way to rid the city of the plague was to punish the murderer of Laius. Oedipus learned the truth, blinded himself, and was exiled by Creon, Jocasta's brother. Does Oedipus blind himself so that he cannot see what he has done, a symbolic castration displaced from below, so that he will be unable to see Laius and Jocasta when he meets them in the underworld? Or is it a regression to his own intrauterine blind state? Whatever the meanings, this is Oedipus' response to his being the patricide and then oedipal victor and sexual possessor of his mother. Jocasta, the mother-wife, commits suicide when she learns of what has occurred. Their two sons, Eteocles and Polynices, at first agree to rule alternate years over Thebes, but they come to blows and are slain. Creon becomes king—he is both Oedipus' uncle and his brother-in-law. He permits Eteocles to be buried, but decrees that Polynices' body shall be left for the vultures. Antigone buries Polynices and is condemned to be buried alive, despite the pleading of Creon's son, who loves her. After Antigone's death, Creon's son attempts to kill his father, and then commits suicide. Creon's wife commits suicide, and the story ends when Creon acknowledges that the rule of his house has been destroyed—the twilight of the gods.

It is important to note that Wagner does not believe that the relationship between Oedipus and Jocasta is a crime. The crime is homicide—it is the murder of Laius that leads to the marriage of Oedipus and Jocasta. Ultimately, the murder of Laius leads to the destruction of the state. In a sense, by their suicide and blinding, Jocasta and Oedipus abrogate all responsibility toward the state, preoccupied only with their own situation. The ship of state with no one at the helm runs aground. In the end, everyone is dead (Rather, 1979). They leave no descendants.

Without going into Wagner's extension of the Oedipus story to political structures, the emphasis on death, murder, deception, and envy-greed in the operas can enable us to gain new insights into the Oedipus plays themselves. Thus, the incestuous union between Siegmund and Sieglinde, like that between Oedipus and Jocasta, "is unnatural only by convention and not by nature" (Rather, 1979, p. 55). The overthrow of the state or existing rule by Antigone, and of the corrupt order of the gods by Siegfried, are both acts of saviors (revolutionaries), and each is the child of an incestuous union. Siegfried and Antigone were Wagner's parallels.

Sabina Spielrein published a paper on "Destruction as the Basis of Becoming" in 1912. Only when the world had returned to its origins could it be saved. "In symbolic form this is represented by the return of the ring (life) to its original home, out of which it was taken" (1912, cited by Rather, 1979, p. 149). Perhaps this is the meaning of *The Ring*—beginning in water and then returning to water—a life course trajectory. This includes the oedipal phase, where Siegfried renders Wotan impotent by shattering his upraised lance with his sword, then passing through the magic fire and consummating his union with Brünnhilde. In doing so, the boy recognizes that he must not sacrifice his manhood in deference to his father.

Wagner wrote to Liszt in 1853 that *The Ring* encompassed the beginning and the end of the world, and I would add, of the life course. What is true of the individual, Wagner seems to say, is true of society. The death of the gods, thus, is the end of the life course of the individual and of society, and reflects pessimism about human invulnerability and immortality. We live today in a society with the highest prison population in the world, greater than that of South Africa or the former Soviet Union. Per capita, we use more of the world's resources than any other nation, yet we harbor large populations of very poor people; tuberculosis, the disease of poverty, is on the rise again. The land, air, and sea have become seriously polluted in the name of "progress." Too many of our resources go to building armaments rather than providing such things as prenatal care. There is a loss of belief in the possibility of changing any of our problems. The government is no longer regarded as being an effective instrument of change. It is hardly surprising that the images we create in art, in painting, theater, poetry, fiction, and the movies, are images of darkness and destruction, of the end of the world. In other words, we live in a world very close in reality to Wagner's intellectual and artistic world as set out in *The Ring*.

Yet Wagner's final statement in *The Ring* is not one of despair. "Instead we hear in its closing bars a harmonious blending of motifs associated with Brünnhilde and Siegfried, with the feminine and masculine principles, a triumphant synthesis of opposites" (Rather, 1979, p. 182).

In retrospect then, it looks as if Wagner's life consisted of repeated oedipal victories and the emotions attendant upon them. His multiple affairs with the wives of men who supported his work were repeated enactments of the oedipal victory. His parents' infidelities were a part of Wagner's childhood, and became in a sense an organizing theme of their son's life. It is not surprising then that the punishment for oedipal victory would be death. This thematic perseveration runs throughout his music and may be the basis of his innate pessimism.

Again, I wish to emphasize that these possible linkages, correlations, and formulations do not explain his musical, literary, and philosophical genius; they may give direction to it and we have seen how Wagner attempted to explore these in his internal and his external creations.

One brief note about the use of myth. In prior work on Thomas Chatterton, a young man who committed suicide in his late teens and whose father died before Chatterton's birth, I found that Chatterton's need to invent a history that antedated his existence seemed to be related to his desire to re-create a life with a father he did not know. In some ways, I believe Wagner may well have been drawn to myth for a similar reason. Behind Geyer, the more prosaic "psychological father" of Wagner's childhood, lay the mythic image of Carl Friedrich Wagner, known and unknown, remembered and forgotten. It is possible to see in Wotan a synthesis of these two fathers, the mystical godhead, and the ruler with very ordinary human foibles whose power is shattered by his grandson, who in the process drags down the whole social order into the abyss.

REFERENCES

Ewans, M. (1982), *Wagner and Aeschylus: The Ring and the Oresteia.* New York & Cambridge, U.K.: Cambridge University Press.

Goldman, A., & Sprinchorn, E. (1964), *Wagner on Music and Drama: A Compendium of Richard Wagner's Prose Works,* tr. H. Ashton Ellis. New York: Da Capo Press.

Kobbé, G. (1919), *The Definitive Kobbé's Opera Book,* ed. Earl of Harewood. New York: G. P. Putnam's Sons, 1987.

Magee, B. (1968), *Aspects of Wagner.* Oxford & New York: Oxford University Press, 1988.

Mander, R., & Mitchenson, J. (1977), *The Wagner Companion.* New York: Hawthorn Books.

Michaelis-Jena, R. (1970), *The Brothers Grimm.* New York: Praeger.

Millington, B. (1987), *Wagner.* New York: Vintage Books.

Newman, E. (1933–1947), *The Life of Richard Wagner,* Vol. 2. New York: Cambridge University Press, 1976.

Pollock, G. H. (1982), The mourning-liberation process and creativity: The case of Kaethe Kollwitz. *The Annual of Psychoanalysis,* 10:333–353. New York: International Universities Press.

―――― (1986), Oedipus examined and reconsidered: The myth, the developmental stage, the universal theme, the conflict and the complex. *The Annual of Psychoanalysis,* 14:77–106. Madison, CT: International Universities Press.

―――― (1989), *The Mourning-Liberation Process,* Vols. 1 & 2. Madison, CT: International Universities Press.

Rank, O. (1912), *The Incest Theme in Literature and Legend.* Baltimore: Johns Hopkins University Press, 1992.

Rather, L. J. (1979), *The Dream of Self-Destruction: Wagner's Ring and the Modern World.* Baton Rouge: Louisiana State University Press.

―――― (1990), *Reading Wagner—A Study in the History of Ideas.* Baton Rouge: Louisiana State University Press.

Sabor, R. (1989), *The Real Wagner.* London: Sphere Books.

Shaw, G. B. (1911), *The Perfect Wagnerite: A Commentary on the Nibelung's Ring,* 2nd ed. New York: Brentano.

Wagner, R. (1856), Letter to August Rockel, August 23, 1856. In: *Richard Wagner an August Rockel,* ed. La Mara [Ida Maria Lipsius]. Leipzig: Breitkopt & Härtel Verlag, 1903.

―――― (1895–1899), *Richard Wagner's Prose Works,* Vols. 1–8, tr. W. A. Ellis. London: Kegan Paul, Trench, Trubner.

―――― (1870), *My Life,* tr. A. Gran, ed. M. Whittall. New York: Cambridge University Press, 1983.

Watson, D. (1979), *Richard Wagner.* New York: Schirmer Books.

6

Dwarfs, Giants, Dragons, and Other Body Distortions in Wagner's Operas

Eric A. Plaut, M.D.

Body–ego distortions abound in Richard Wagner's work. There are animal shapes, odd sizes, wounds. There are also displacements in time and space. That Wagner's own bodily concerns importantly influenced this aspect of his work can be inferred both from his life's story and from the fact that the distorted bodily images are almost always male (the Rhinemaidens and Kundry are the only exceptions). Four major themes from Wagner's life are reflected in these distortions: (1) His own health problems, particularly his erysipelas. (2) His love of animals, vegetarianism, and fervent antivivisectionism. (3) His concerns about his paternity. (4) His many personal wanderings. These four themes appear repeatedly in all of Wagner's mature operatic tragedies, especially in *The Ring*. My intent here is to demonstrate the connections between the operatic expression of these themes and Wagner's personal life.

Midnineteenth century operatic audiences were not accustomed to grotesques on stage (Rigoletto was a rare exception), but they were accustomed to them elsewhere (Fiedler, 1978). Not only was this the era of greatest popularity of "freak" shows but the deformed figured prominently in the works of writers such as Poe, Hugo, Twain, and Dickens. Such distortions, commonly found in dreams, are, of course,

Material from this chapter has appeared in Dr. Plaut's *Grand Opera: Mirror of the Western Mind*, Ivan R. Dee, Chicago, 1993. It is reprinted here with permission of the publisher.

characteristic of primary process thinking. Influenced by Nietzsche and Schopenhauer, Wagner saw both instinctual forces and their manifestation in dreams as the road to enlightenment and truth. He had a remarkable capacity for transforming his primitive character structure and phantasies into reality. In his artistic expressions, through his creative genius, this resulted in some unique masterpieces. In his personal life, in areas like sexuality and finances, it led to much chaos, not to mention amoral, antisocial, and illegal behavior.

In his infancy Wagner was surrounded by violence and illness. Prussia and Austria were fighting Napoleon at the time and Leipzig, his birthplace, was where Napoleon was defeated. Indeed, it was the outbreak of typhus following that battle, when Richard was only 6 months old, which killed Wagner's father. Even before then, at age 2 months, he had been taken by his mother on a dangerous 100-mile journey through enemy-held territory to visit Ludwig Geyer (whom his mother married 9 months after Wagner's father's death). Six months later a sister was born. Wagner was a sickly child. The first attacks of erysipelas came before he was 10 years old.

We can, of course, only speculate how this early exposure to violence, sickness, and death affected him. Bodily preoccupations, however, played a prominent role throughout his life. At various times he had severe bladder troubles, constipation, stomach aches, and insomnia, but most debilitating of all was the recurrent erysipelas. Nineteenth century physicians had a remarkably thorough and accurate understanding of the gross and microscopic pathology, of the symptoms and course, and of the contagiousness of the illness. Unfortunately, their treatments were extremely primitive (Lawrence, 1827). In the first half of the nineteenth century it was frequently treated with incisions and blood-letting. We do not know if Wagner was subjected to such treatments as a child. Later on he went to spas for rigorous treatment via diet, baths, and so on which he described as "water torture." When an attack involved his face he would sometimes not go outside for long periods of time until the attack had passed. When his bride-to-be, Minna, kissed him on the lips during an attack of facial erysipelas, it was, for Richard, then age 21, a token of the specialness of her love for him.

The deformed body is almost ever-present throughout *The Ring*. The opening scene of *Das Rheingold* consists of the interaction between the Rhinemaidens—mermaids—and the dwarf Alberich. They tell him he is "a scaly, spotted lecher of small stature." In the next scene we are introduced to the one-eyed Wotan and the giants Fafner and Fasolt. Indeed, no humans at all appear in *Das Rheingold*, the rest of the characters are all gods and goddesses. We have to wait until *Die Walküre* for ordinary humans.

Wagner's erysipelas was a wound that would not heal. Although that theme appears only indirectly in *The Ring*—the World Ash Tree never recovers from Wotan's removal of one of its branches—it is an important theme in both *Tristan und Isolde* and in *Parsifal.* It requires Isolde's magical powers to heal Tristan's wound before the opening of the opera and she arrives too late to heal him again at the end. Amfortas too has a wound that will not heal until Parsifal brings his magical power to bear on it. Besides his many bodily complaints, Wagner also suffered repeated bouts of depression, at times with suicidal thoughts. The wound that would not heal was undoubtedly psychical as well as physical.

With the exception of the Walkyries' mounts (which are rarely displayed on stage), no animals appear in *Das Rheingold* or *Die Walküre*. In *Siegfried*, a dragon, a bear, and a bird all play significant parts. Animals were important to Wagner throughout his life. From a very early age on he had shown a great love for them, often bringing stray or wounded ones home. As a small child he had reacted violently to seeing a butcher slaughter an ox. He kept a variety of pets, but dogs were his constant companions. We know of eleven favorites. In a letter regarding a visit to Wagner, Liszt described how Wagner "rolls on the floor, caressing his dog Peps and talking perpetual nonsense to him" (cited in Hodson, 1984, p. 163). He was once bitten on the hand by a bulldog, and was consequently unable to compose for some time, but continued to cherish the animal. When his ex-wife, Minna, died he did not attend the funeral. A few days later, however, on learning that his dog, Pohl, had died, he had the dog disinterred and held a solemn funeral for it.

Closely connected to this love of animals was Wagner's vegetarianism and antivivisectionism. Late in life he increasingly adopted a Christian identity. He viewed the symbolic offering of flesh and blood, in communion, as Christ's exhortation that his followers be vegetarians. A return to natural food was the only hope for the salvation of mankind. Similarly, his life-long antivivisectionism also acquired a moral–religious dimension in his later years. Vivisection was wrong because it led to the use of animals to try to find a cure for syphilis, and syphilis was punishment for sexual transgressions. This strain of Puritanism was the opposite side of Wagner's adulterous promiscuity and the endorsement of incest that runs throughout *The Ring*. It was already evident in *Tann-häuser* and reached its height in *Parsifal*. Wagner never resolved this conflict in himself. The heart attack that killed him at age 70 was proba- bly precipitated by a violent argument with his wife Cosima over his interest in a young girl.

Fafner appeared in *Das Rheingold* as a giant. In *Siegfried* he has been magically transformed into a dragon. Such human–animal transforma- tions were, until the Judeo-Christian tradition, part of most reli- gions—the Indian, the Egyptian, the Greek, the Central African, the American Indian and the Nordic, from which Wagner drew for *The Ring* story. Wagner first used the concept in *Die Feen*, where Ada has been transformed into a doe; then in *Lohengrin*, where Godfrey has been transformed into a swan. The swan has often been a symbol of nobility (e.g., the Greek Leda and the French Le Chevalier au Cygne), and Godfrey was a noble figure. The noble swan reappears in *Parsifal*. Fafner was a nasty giant and remains nasty as a dragon. Fafner and Siegfried can converse, because Fafner is a transformed giant. But it is only when he has tasted Fafner's blood that Siegfried can converse with the birds.

The birds speak the real truth to him, including prophecy of his future. Having partaken of Fafner's blood, Siegfried can now also hear the truth as men speak; he hears what Mime means, not what Mime says. From the cultural perspective Wagner here reflects the Romantic- era ideal of man living in perfect harmony with nature. From the psycho- logical perspective, human communication with animals reflects prever- bal, preoedipal communication. Just as *The Ring* has many elements of preoedipal world destruction phantasies (e.g., in the final dénoument), it also has many elements of preoedipal symbiotic unity and bliss (e.g., in the merger of Siegmund and Sieglinde, of Siegfried and Brünnhilde, and in Siegfried's relation to nature). Birds appear again in *Götterdäm- merung*. But whereas the woodbird in *Siegfried* is a symbol of life and love, the birds that carry Wotan the message of Siegfried's death are ravens, symbols of scavenging and death. Their names are Thought and Memory. Thus they are tokens of the verbal, of the oedipal, and, for Wagner, of doom.

The other important animal in *The Ring* is the wild bear which Siegfried, in his first appearance, drags along to frighten Mime. Sieg- fried is totally open about his contempt for Mime:

[W]hen I watch you standing, shuffling and shambling,

servilely stooping, squinting and blinking,
I long to seize you by your nodding neck
and make an end of your obscene blinking! [Act I, Scene 1].

The words are unmistakeably similar to those Wagner used to describe Jews in his many anti-Semitic statements. It was no coincidence that Wagner chose a bear to threaten Mime, the Jew. When Wagner devised a family crest for himself it consisted of a vulture carrying a shield with the constellation The Great Bear upon it (Deathridge and Dahlhaus, 1984).

Wagner's crest from the title page of the first private edition of *Mein Leben* (1871).

In German, the word *Geier* (pronounced the same as Geyer) means vulture or hawk. The constellation Great Bear has another name, the Wagon. The wagon driver is the "wagener." Wagner senior had died when Richard was 6 months old. Geyer was the only father he knew. Although Geyer died when Wagner was only 8, Richard continued to use the name Richard Geyer until he was 14.

Whether Geyer or Wagner senior was actually Richard's father remains unclear. What matters is not that we don't know, but that Wagner didn't know. We do know now that Geyer did not have any Jewish blood. Wagner, however, all his life thought that he might have. The connection between the bear and Wagner's feeling about his lost father was already clear at age 24 when he started work on a libretto entitled *The Happy Bear Family or Woman's Wiles Outsmarted*. There is no evidence that the timing of the name change had anything to do with Geyer's supposed Jewish blood, since Wagner was never openly anti-Semitic until his thirties (Katz, 1986).

Despite rejecting Geyer's name and his supposed Jewishness, Wagner clearly also identified with Geyer, who had been a friend of Wagner senior. Repeatedly, one might say compulsively, Wagner seduced his friends' wives. Additionally, despite his virulent anti-Semitism, he maintained close personal and professional relationships with many Jews.

Additional evidence for the importance to Wagner of his unclear paternity is the repeated appearance in his work of the significance of names and paternity. The theme appears first in his early opera *Die Feen* (age 20), again in *Lohengrin* (age 33), and once more in *Parsifal* (first draft age 44, final completion age 69). The questions, bear or vulture, Wagner or Geyer, maintained their significance throughout Wagner's life.

The next character to appear on stage after Siegfried and the bear is Wotan. Only now, in his final appearance in *The Ring*, he is a wanderer. This theme, the body dislocated in space, also recurs throughout Wagner's works. It appears in his first completed opera, *Die Feen*, is central to his first mature work, *Der Fliegende Holländer*, and then appears in all but two of his subsequent works, *Tannhäuser, Lohengrin, The Ring*, and *Parsifal*. In *Die Feen*, Arindal lives in both the real world and in fairyland. The Dutchman is doomed to roam the seas. Tannhäuser lives both in Venusberg and in the real world. Lohengrin must remain away from Montsalvat or lose his holy power. Wotan wanders the earth, searching for a solution to his dilemma. Parsifal has traveled restlessly, not knowing where he is from. The theme is, thus, present in six of Wagner's thirteen operas.

The pervasiveness of the theme in his operas parallels the facts of his life. In infancy and childhood, owing to the war and his mother's relationship with Geyer, there were multiple moves between Leipzig and Dresden. As an adult, he was constantly traveling, conducting, and overseeing operatic productions. Repeatedly he was forced to move by hotly pursuing creditors. From ages 36 to 48 he was in exile because of his political activities. From ages 52 to 57 he was again exiled from Bavaria because of his illicit relationship with Cosima Liszt von Bülow.

At various times, he had his primary residence in Germany, Austria, France, Latvia, Switzerland, and Italy.

Richard Wagner's endless wandering was paralleled by his endless womanizing. Compulsive promiscuity is not an uncommon phenomenon. Wagner's penchant for the wives of close friends is unusual. Taken together with the endorsement of incest that pervades *The Ring*, it is strongly suggestive of a massive need to deny oedipal castration anxiety. This ultimate fear of bodily damage appears only in *Parsifal*, Wagner's last opera.

Although some of the themes in *Parsifal* have antecedents in *Tannhäuser* and *Lohengrin*, Wagner's final opera is in most ways a radical departure from his other operas. No longer does the man seek salvation through the unqualified love of a woman. Here, quite to the contrary, it is only by rejecting the woman that the man can find salvation. The woman is no longer constant and loving. Here she is erratic and deceitful in her behavior, yet also truthful in her words. In many ways what had been a split image in *Tannhäuser* has now been fused into one figure. Klingsor, the embodiment of evil, derives his power from his invulnerability to woman's wiles; he has castrated himself.

By resisting Kundry's wiles, Parsifal not only achieves his own salvation, but also is able to heal Amfortas' wound and save the Company of the Holy Grail. In the end Kundry dies and the men find salvation in their bond to each other and their Christian faith.

Diagnosing at a distance is always a risky enterprise. However, the vast amount of information available about Wagner is highly suggestive that he suffered from some form of character disorder (Chessick, 1983). Whenever we try to understand this kind of personality structure the question arises to what extent the preoedipal elements reflect developmental failures and to what extent they reflect regressive phenomena resulting from inability to come to grips with oedipal issues and castration anxiety. I believe there are two pieces of evidence suggesting that the regressive element was central in Wagner's development.

The first is the developmental sequence of themes in his operas. In *Der Fliegende Holländer, Tannhäuser,* and *Lohengrin* the man can be saved only through the totally unquestioning love of an earth-mother figure. In *The Ring* the incestuous oedipal triumph is the attempted solution, but it leads to disaster. In *Parsifal*, his last work, Wagner finally addresses his deepest conflict, his inability to identify with, and reconcile with, a father figure. The earlier phantasies are of an omnipotent, all-giving mother. Next come the phantasies of oedipal triumph and the recognition of the failure of that solution. Finally, the mother is renounced and reconciliation with the father is achieved.

The second piece of evidence that Wagner's character did not reflect primarily early developmental failures was his remarkable capacity for concentrated work and continued investment in a task over long periods of time. *The Ring* was a twenty-year project. The kind of ego strength required for such an accomplishment is unlikely for one whose personality structure is primarily characterized by developmental failures. Such areas of great ego strength, in a character structure with many primitive features, are most likely reflective of considerable successful maturation marred by severe regression.

Before closing I should like to touch briefly on Wagner's music. In many ways his compositional techniques give expression to the same issues as do his libretti. Just as animals are transformed into people and vice versa, so his motifs are constantly undergoing transformations, mergers with other motifs, inversions, relocations. Just as his operatic characters are unreliably located in time and space, so his meters are constantly changing, his phrases are of unpredictable and constantly changing length. The unique character of individual instruments is obscured by having them play in unison (Adorno, 1981). The sense of lack of bodily integrity and of ego boundaries is thus in the music as well as in the libretti.

After almost a hundred years, Freud's dictum "The self is first and foremost a bodily self" retains its heuristic value (Freud, 1923; MacIntosh, 1986). In this paper I have attempted to illustrate the extent to which bodily concerns remained foremost to Wagner in both his life and his work. In Act I, Scene 2 of *Götterdämmerung* he had Siegfried say it for him: "I inherited only my own body and that I consume as I live."

REFERENCES

Adorno, T. (1981), *In Search of Wagner.* Trowbridge/Esher, U.K.: NLB, Redburn Burn.
Chessick, R. (1983), The Ring: Richard Wagner's dream of pre-oedipal destruction. *Amer. J. Psychoanal.*, 43:361–374.
Deathridge, J., & Dahlhaus, C. (1984), *The New Grove Wagner.* New York: W. W. Norton.

Fiedler, L. (1978), *Freaks.* New York: Simon & Schuster.

Freud, S. (1923), The ego and the id. *Standard Edition,* 19:1–59. London: Hogarth Press, 1961.

Hodson, P. (1984), *Who's Who in Wagner.* New York: Macmillan.

Katz, J. (1986), *The Darker Side of Genius.* Hanover, NH: University Press of New England.

Lawrence, W. (1827), On erysipelas. In: *Medical-Chirurgical Transations,* Vol. 13. London: G. Woodfall.

MacIntosh, D. (1986), The ego and self in the thought of Sigmund Freud. *Internat. J. Psycho-Anal.,* 67:429–448.

Wagner, R. (1871), *Mein Leben.* Leipzig.

7

Women in Wagner's Operas

Herta Glaz

Wagner, in his autobiography, *Mein Leben* (1871), describes a part of his childhood in an all-female household, his attachment to his older sisters, one of whom served as a model for the sister in *Rienzi*, one of his first important operas written after his sister's death, a loss which greatly affected him. He also speaks of his early erotic fantasies stimulated by the surrounding females. All his life he distinguished between love and lust, and expressed agony over tormenting sexual drives connected with feelings of guilt and hope for redemption.

My interest in the female roles in Wagner's operas started during my last year at the Academy of Music in Vienna. In spite of my young age (not quite 19), my teacher, Rosa Papier, suggested that I should take part in a master class at the Salzburg Mozarteum given by the famous Anna Bahr von Mildenburg who had sung leading roles in Bayreuth and had worked closely with Cosima Wagner. Mildenburg worked with her students on musical as well as dramatic styles and interpretation. That summer turned out to be a most valuable one for me because Wagnerian mezzo roles became a part of my repertoire. My debut at my first engagement in Breslau was Erda in *Das Rheingold* and my first roles in the United States with the Chicago Opera were Fricka, in *Die Walküre*, and Brangäne in *Tristan und Isolde*, and I was fortunate to sing in the unsurpassed stellar cast of Kirsten Flagstad, Lauritz Melchior, Marjorie Lawrence, and Alexander Kipnis.

Inspired, I studied the libretti and music of Wagner's operas, his personal life, his relations to the women who inspired his works, and reflected upon his own attitude and expectation of women.

It is astounding how black-and-white his female characters are, stereotypical images which go like a red thread through his works: the spotless, immaculate, pious, serving, self-sacrificing women, and in stark contrast, the seductresses—evil, man-destroying women who are also sorceresses. They are symbolic figures and don't seem to be real. They don't seem like human beings in whom good and bad qualities mix. Kundry in *Parsifal,* is both good and bad but is a dual personality and is either one or the other. Eva in *Die Meistersinger* is an exception; this is the composer's only realistic work, based on the life of the great German poet, Hans Sachs.

It seems to us quite extraordinary that Pogner offers his only child Eva as a prize to the winner of a singing contest, in which the winner, as in Tannhäuser, has to write his own song—both text and music—just as Wagner did. The question is: did Eva's happiness mean so little to her father that he would give her in marriage to anyone who won the contest?

Lohengrin, who offers Elsa his hand in marriage, warns her never to ask him his name, where he comes from, or who his people are. She has to accept him without suspicion or even inner doubts. When, after Ortrud's insinuations, she does ask him the forbidden questions, he answers her in the presence of the knights, and then departs forever in punishment of her doubts. Heroes, like demigods, must have a mysterious, never-to-be-known past. Legends, northern myths, the Niebelungen-Saga, the Arthurian legend of the Holy Grail (after Wolfram von Eschenbach's *Parsifal*) appeared to be not only the center of Wagner's interest, they also enabled him to express his social concepts, ideas, and philosophy. His female characters were not only his own concepts, but corresponded with the romantic period of Wagner's time. The condition of women in the nineteenth and early twentieth century was not one of freedom. Many times daughters were married off without their consent. Sophie, in *Der Rosenkavalier* promised in marriage to the old Baron Ochs, says to Octavian, "You are a man and will remain what you are, but I first need a man in order to be someone, therefore I am very much indebted to that man."

If they had no suitors, daughters were often a worry to their fathers. Additional incentives like the dowry were given away with the daughter. Such was the status of many women in Western society prior to the twentieth century. While women were quite often powerful and influential, it was the man who dominated and initiated action. One cannot help but think of the Biblical version of the creation; of Adam, and God's seeming afterthought of forming Eve out of Adam's rib to give him a companion.

All central actors in Wagner's operas are men, and so are the titles of his operas *Rienzi, Lohengrin, Parsifal, Tannhäuser,* and *Der Fliegende Holländer.* Even Tristan takes precedence over Isolde, although they play equal parts in the drama. King Marke, after he discovers the love relationship between Tristan and Isolde, does not reproach his wife, but blames Tristan for his breach of friendship and honor. Even the title of the *Ring* cycle's third opera *Die Walküre* does not carry the individual name of Brünnhilde as the title, but rather the name Wotan assigned collectively to his nine daughters, the children of his extramarital union with Erda; even though Brünnhilde was his favorite daughter, they are all executors of Wotan's will. When Brünnhilde disobeys his orders she is severely punished, condemned to sleep surrounded by flames (symbolic of the patriarchal society), until a hero awakens her.

Let us look at the different female characters: Elisabeth prays day and night for Tannhäuser's salvation and his renunciation of Venus, who held him with erotic lust in contrast to the spiritual love which Elisabeth represents and for which he is longing. The yearning for redemption in nearly all his works is like an outcry of Wagner himself, who struggled with his supercharged erotic disposition. Nietzsche speaks of the "Wollust der Hölle" (lust of Hell) not to be stilled by any fulfillment. Elisabeth gives her life, dies of a broken heart, and prays for Tannhäuser in Heaven. Tannhäuser, kneeling at her open coffin, exclaims "Heilige Elisabeth, bete für mich!" ("Holy Elisabeth, pray for me!"). He dies, and is saved. The counterpart to Elisabeth is Venus. She seduced Tannhäuser, and as Mephistopheles in Goethe's *Faust* loses the soul of the dying Gretchen, so does Venus lose Tannhäuser through the power of Elisabeth's love.

Senta in *Der Fliegende Holländer* is entranced and obsessed by the fate of the legendary sailor, who was condemned by Satan to roam the seas for all eternity, unless he found a maiden faithful unto death. The Dutchman, who is permitted to land every seven years, meets Senta. She swears she will save him. He warns her of the curse that if she should not fulfill her oath, she too would be damned forever. His ship quickly leaves the shore, and Senta, running after him, drowns in the sea. He is redeemed through her love; united they ascend to Heaven. Is this what Wagner expected from a woman? It is not without significance that in the first draft of the opera, the name of the sacrificing woman was not Senta but Minna—his first wife. Minna, a successful, beautiful young actress, gave up her career and suffered through Wagner's most difficult years of poverty, debts, and exile because of his revolutionary activities. There were quarrels and separations between Richard and Minna, but Minna always returned until she realized Wagner's deep involvement with Mathilde von Wesendonck, whom he called "an angel sent by God," and spoke of as an otherworldly happiness. Years later, after Minna and Wagner were divorced, he spoke of Minna as a very good woman who, however, never understood him. Wesendonck was the greatest influence on his creativity and his most profound love. She inspired *Tristan und Isolde* and her suggestions led to *Parsifal* and *Die Meistersinger*. She was not the only married woman he got involved with: there were others, including his third wife Cosima, twenty-four years younger than he, who was married and already had children with Wagner's close friend and devoted follower Hans von Bülow.

Completing the list of women who follow their heroes into death: Sieglinde in *Die Walküre,* after Siegmund's death postpones her wish to die, only after giving birth to her and Siegmund's child. This child, Siegfried—the result of the incestuous union between brother and sister—will be the hero, fearless of the flames surrounding Brünnhilde. And Brünnhilde herself, after Siegfried's death, rushes into the burning funeral pyre. Thus, she returns the fateful ring to the Rhinemaidens.

Isolde follows Tristan, who dies in her arms. She dies the death of love, "Den Liebestod." Contrary to Elisabeth in *Tannhäuser* and Senta in *The Flying Dutchman,* who rise to a Christian heaven, Isolde, in her last words, seems to dissolve into nature, submerging in the waves, air, and fragrance, suggesting a pantheistic philosophy. Reunion of lovers in death is a recurring late-romantic concept. Tristan speaks of a "Todestrunk'ne Welt" (Death-drunken world). Mysticism and metaphysics play an important role in German romantic literature.

A character different from Wagner's heroines is Brangäne in *Tristan* who personifies the servant-companion living only for her mistress, with no personal life. The constrained nature of women's lives before emancipation was a not uncommon phenomenon. Romanticism made Wagner's female characters understandable.

How much has Fricka in *Das Rheingold* and *Die Walküre* in common with Minna? Fricka, the goddess of law and justice, the upholder of the marriage vow, reproaches Wotan for his extramarital relations and his roaming of the world to look for new adventures. In *Die Walküre*, Fricka wins her argument for the outcome of the fight between Hunding, the unloved husband of Sieglinde and the twin brother of Siegmund. The offender Siegmund should die and Hunding, the husband, should live. She is enraged at the incest. "When was it heard of that brother and sister lusted after each other?" she asks, and Wotan replies, "Heut hast du's erlebt" ("Today you have witnessed it.") Wotan had to give in to Fricka's moral arguments, but he has both Siegmund and Hunding killed. Did Wagner take revenge by never having Fricka, who probably symbolized his wife Minna, appear again in either *Siegfried* or *Götterdämmerung*, and thus out of his life and forgotten; marriage certainly was never holy to Wagner. He despised what he considered bourgeois attitudes.

Then there are the maidens given away as payment, such as Freia, who was given to the giants who built Valhalla. She was rescued only by the gods' realization that Freia alone could provide the apples they needed to stay young. The attempt to replace her with gold cunningly stolen from the dwarf Alberich, on Loge's advice, was the beginning of the fight for power over the world and the end of the gods.

To bring this short, obviously incomplete presentation of Wagner's women in opera to a conclusion, I would like to quote Wagner, who once stated: "Eroticism is the prerequisite to all artistic creation." His genius was his extraordinary ability to sublimate his positive feelings as well as his most painful, disappointing experiences into artistic masterpieces. He expresses his philosophy of the world in symbolic, fairytalelike stories. He created a new form of opera theater, Das Gesamtkunstwerk, in which his own libretti were of equal importance to him as his revolutionary musical expression. As Thomas Mann once wrote, "Wagner's music illustrated his texts." He achieved a unique synthesis of poetry and music unknown before, but through it he reveals his innermost life. In a letter to Franz Liszt, he writes, "Das intimste erfährst du wenn du den Tristan kennenlernst"—"You will gain the most intimate kind of understanding when you come to know Tristan." In Wagner's world, man's salvation comes through women's love and sacrifice.

REFERENCE

Wagner, R. (1871), *Mein Leben*, tr. F. Bruckmann. New York: Dodd, Mead, 1911.

8

Health and Medicine in Wagner's Germany, 1820–1890

Günter B. Risse, M.D., Ph.D.

In 1884, a year after Wagner's death, the prominent physician William Osler wrote a brief report about his European visit. At the time, Germany was already universally acknowledged as the cradle of modern scientific medicine. "Not one of the European medical centers can compare with Berlin in the progress which has been made in the past decade," he observed (Osler, 1884, p. 170). Indeed, during the last quarter of the nineteenth century, students from throughout the world flocked to famous German universities and their laboratories to learn about the new basic disciplines underlying medicine and the exacting methods of laboratory science. Lavish governmental expenditures had created new research and care facilities which were the envy of Europe. "There may be disadvantages in the paternal form of government under which our German colleagues live," added Osler, "but these are not evident in a survey of their university and hospital arrangements" (Osler, 1884, p. 170).

Such high praise stands in stark contrast with the perceived backwardness of German medicine a generation earlier, when the young Wagner began suffering from sporadic skin infections. Although at times hostile to physicians, Wagner thus witnessed the profound metamorphosis which took place in nineteenth-century German medicine. For purposes of simplification, three main stages can be discerned. The first comprises the decades before the 1848 revolution in which Wagner was an active participant. The second covers the postrevolutionary years until 1871, representing more than a quarter-century of economic progress and eventual political unification during which our composer wrote his operatic tetralogy. Finally, the third period coincides with the development of the Bayreuth Circle and Wagner's final years (Anderson, 1980).

"BIEDERMEIER" MEDICINE

Historians of medicine have characterized the decades before 1848 as the reign of "Biedermeier" medicine, a reference to a character in a popular satirical poem, who gave that era its cultural nickname (Bleker, 1988). Mr. Biedermeier was a member of the propertied and educated class, submissive to the authorities, sanctimonious, and merciless toward the poor. This particular label stuck and came to depict a whole generation of middle-class Germans known for their class consciousness, fainthearted liberalism in the midst of political timidity, social hypocrisy, and educational elitism. A similar characterization is also applicable to a restricted group of friendly family physicians, dressed in flowered waistcoats, who for an annual retainer functioned more as friends and confidants than healers to the families they attended. The traditional approach was to individualize medical practice within this private framework. Such family physicians typically took care of their patients during a lifetime of service and based their relationships on an intimate knowledge of the life-style, culture, and social relations of those whom they attended (Heischkel Artelt, 1967).

In Central Europe, the post-Napoleonic period witnessed a significant expansion of the medical marketplace with more members of the middle class becoming candidates for professional care (Broman, 1989). Thus, the demand for medical services increased sharply in the cities, and constant feuding among health care professionals over patient patronage, consultations, and fees became de rigueur. "Physicians lived like spiders, each in its own web, displaying even when satiated the proverbial hostility of such insects," recalled one of them (Richter, 1873). Fearing a life of poverty and intellectual stagnation, few new medical graduates ventured into the countryside. For the beginning practitioner, medical practice meant the specter of "seven Egyptian years of famine" before achieving enough remuneration to survive in middle-class dignity. Not surprisingly, a medical profession still divided along traditional divisions of physicians, surgeons, and barbers possessed only limited authority and power. Alternative healing schemes and quackery flourished.

By the 1830s, however, an overwhelming majority of German medical graduates chose their state certification as a Medico-Chirurg or physician-surgeon, thus combining both medicine and surgery in their quest for enhanced status and cultural recognition. Success in pain control and the feasibility of useful albeit limited surgical procedures had given surgery new prestige. Scientifically, they still lacked a coherent theoretical base, with a number of medical systems competing for acceptance. Thus, many physicians embarked on a program of observations at the sickbed and the anatomical dissection table, collecting, labeling, and classifying disease. Their descriptive approach—defined as "naturhistorisch"—stood in marked contrast with the speculative spirit of the preceding romantic era. As before, professional medical authority was based on claims that physicians possessed superior knowledge of vital forces and functions. Therefore, practitioners could successfully manage health and disease conditions with the traditional "regimen," including changes in life-style, and the prescription of certain drugs (Bleker, 1983).

Within such a competitive setting, German physicians tried hard to survive as individual entrepreneurs, but the increased rivalry forced them to also demand protection, security, and privileges identified with governmental employees or *Beamten*. Indeed, civil service became an honorable alternative in some thirty German states which provided a limited number of positions at court, cities, and towns, the latter linked with poor relief. University professors and municipal physicians were the highest paid. There were also public assistance doctors as part of the civil services of more than thirty independent German states. Soon, nepotism and the hunt for state-paid positions became widespread and dependency upon the benevolence of the authorities created a fertile breeding ground for political intrigue. Since states controlled medical practice through licensing, their arbitrariness generated considerable antagonisms.

This limited professional status of German physicians failed to eliminate a widespread cultural icon: the traditional elitist ideology of *Bildung* or erudition. The neohumanist notion of education as a personal and collective quest for self-development, remained firmly entrenched in the minds of university faculty, students, and the public at large.

Although universities were all state financed and state run, governments did not dictate the content of the curriculum. The search for truth was based on knowledge or Wissenschaft, traditionally philosophy, theology, and the classic languages. From the beginning, the German states had supported a decentralized state university system with academic self-government, Wissenschaft ethos, and a flexible plan of studies culminating in degrees and dissertations based on original research. Within the increasingly competitive environment created by the forces of commerce and industry during the 1830s, German universities developed into valuable instruments of state power and development. At the center of this change were mathematics, the natural sciences, medicine, and modern languages which replaced the previous primacy of philosophy, Latin, and Greek (Paul, 1984).

After the French Revolution, the first step of disease description and identification had already taken place in the hospitals of Paris. Now, efforts got under way to understand the phenomena and mechanisms that produced normal and pathological changes in the human body. Health and medicine were to be equally "scientized," based on true biological principles. New endeavors to understand the mechanisms of biological phenomena culminated in 1839 with the discovery of the cell theory by Theodor Schwann, and the 1840 formulation of a germ theory of disease by Jacob Henle. In 1842, Rudolf Virchow, the famous founder of cell pathology, and Carl Wunderlich, a prominent clinician, called for a "physiological medicine" (Ackerknecht, 1953). Experimental methods had already disclosed a number of laws controlling chemistry and physics. "We must demand that medicine adopt the same method employed in the exact physical sciences," explained Wunderlich. In 1847, a new reductionist program emerged as four notable researchers, Ernst von Bruecke, Herman von Helmholtz, Carl Ludwig, and Emil du Bois Reymond issued a joint manifesto stating that physiology should also be placed "on a chemicophysical foundation" and given "equal scientific rank with physics" (Cranefield, 1966).

Both the Prussian-German customs union of 1834 and the construction of a vast railroad network powerfully stimulated the development of trade and industry. German governments, in turn, instituted wide-ranging reforms designed to improve and modernize their economies. Trade schools, technical institutes, and nonclassical secondary schools mushroomed to provide an adequate general education to citizens aiming for careers in an industrializing society. Moreover, the railroads brought German academics together at regular scientific meetings, facilitating the exchange of ideas. A number of new medical journals began publication at this time.

To protect their professional interests, German physicians established a number of societies and medical associations. Among them was the Verein praktischer Aerzte, established in Berlin (1832), and in the south the Verein bayerischer Aerzte (1841). As expected, members of these organizations focused exclusively on the internal affairs of the medical profession, expressing their desire for a more homogeneous profession and the abolition of the separate categories of health practitioners. In Germany, organized medicine's stated emphasis was on the moral and social aspects of physicianship. They failed, however, to control admission to the profession and to shape the content of medical education.

Upon becoming king in August, 1840, Prussia's Friedrich Wilhelm IV decreed an amnesty for all political offenders, but this period of liberalization only lasted two years. Germany was on the threshold of the industrial age, with thousands of people leaving rural districts and swelling the towns in search of jobs. The movement began in the eastern provinces and spread to the west, dramatically increasing the numbers of registered poor. For the first time, public assistance doctors now came into close contact with the plight of the lower classes, some developing a greater sensitivity for the social problems of their patients. By 1842 the medical society of Cologne estimated that 21,000 of its total population of 75,000 (28%) were so poor that their health care had to be totally paid out of public funds. Another 10,000 craftsmen and clerks—almost 13 percent of the population—could afford medicines but no physician's honorarium. In the course of the 1840s, the public relief funds proved insufficient to cope with the growing number of sick and homeless, and physicians were forced to provide medical assistance to many poor who were not registered, thus forfeiting possible reimbursement for their services.

During the 1840s, the winds of revolutionary change in medical theory were matched by strong demands for reform in medical care. Previous models of assistance now proved totally inadequate in the face of an accelerating industrialization that produced deadly epidemics and massive population shifts from rural to urban areas, from the poor and backward east to the new western centers of commerce. A liberal agenda argued for social justice and equal rights, with proposals for free care in community hospitals and policlinics. Salomon Neumann's new field of social medicine urged the establishment of health as a right. Virchow's vision was to build a society based on the new laws of physiology, with the medical profession as an advocate for the poor and a resource capable of guiding life-styles and work conditions. For Virchow, politics was really medicine applied on a larger scale (Virchow, 1859).

In retrospect it seems clear that the medical reform movement of the 1840s which reflected in part the material insecurity of German physicians and their moral crisis, brought about personal poverty and ruthless competition, interferences from the absolutist bureaucracy, and a loss of public confidence. This reform aimed to improve the status of the medical profession within the context of growing health problems brought about by industrialization and urbanization of the German states. Resentment of the existing oppression by the state resulted in calls for freedom from its control. Thus, Virchow's program was a comprehensive effort to overcome the evils of free competition, remove the lingering caste separation between military and civilian practitioners, and abolish the existing hierarchical order in the profession. A right to practice in all states and self-rule were some of the additional goals (Huerkamp, 1990).

With the passage in 1845 of a Prussian trade act that included physicians in their capacity as private entrepreneurs, strong opposition arose. As employees of the state, physicians would be controlled and protected from open market competition, but their civil rights would be restricted since they could no longer select their places of practice. As tradesmen, however, practitioners could retain their freedom to set fees and escape from the obligatory treatment clause. In numerous petitions and declarations, the medical profession made it clear that its members did not wish to become completely dependent on the government, especially with regard to the setting of adequate wages. It was also pointed out that the authorities should not determine the professional competency of physicians (Blackbourne and Eley, 1984).

THE POSTREVOLUTIONARY YEARS

As 1848 approached, reformers such as Virchow and Naumann realized that, given the social origin of most diseases, private medical practice would never have a great impact on health conditions. The poor suffering from epidemics, alcoholism, and venereal diseases could not be reached in this manner and public health measures, insofar as they existed, were driven from above and thus oppressive and often useless. Medical reform, therefore, had to start from the premise that a solution could not be achieved if no distinctions were made between the health of rich and poor people. The new tool to accomplish this goal was the fledgling scientific medicine based on natural laws equally valid under all social conditions. The use of experimental biology as an autonomous basis for a science of human physiology, pathology, and hygiene became a weapon in the fight for professional respect. A rallying cry for the radicals during the 1848 revolution were demands for a "free and objective science" (Ackerknecht, 1932).

The ideology of scientific medicine was employed to propose equal rights for all Germans to receive medical attention. Guaranteeing equal medical treatment to everyone instead of care based on rank and class, addressed the political and economic liberalism of the 1848 reformers. For this purpose, the reformers insisted on the concept of health as a right of all citizens who possessed the necessary physical and moral strength to be productive. Such a view would replace charity as the basis for medical assistance to the poor. The professional strategy of posing as natural representatives of the poor and solvers of social questions made physicians de facto custodians of the nation's health.

Behind the revolutionary rhetoric, Virchow and the reformers used the newly enlarged scope of medical activities to improve the professional fortunes of Germany's physicians. Like others before them, they argued against both state control and the existing free market in medical practice. Public accountability was rejected. Self-regulation could be achieved through the establishment of corporate professional organizations. Only the state-sanctioned title of *Arzt*—the university-trained and qualified medical practitioner—was to be legally protected. Indeed, the superiority of scientific qualifications alone would guarantee the professional status of physicians. Experimental biology now furnished an autonomous basis for legitimation. Competition with popular healing schemes such as homeopathy and hydropathy would be successful because scientific credentials guaranteed the superior position of university-trained physicians practicing Schulmedizin.

Reaction after the failed revolution nullified previous gains while new constraints were imposed on the medical profession. Article 200 of the Prussian penal code enacted in April 1851 stipulated that physicians were legally required to offer medical assistance, Kurierzwang. Refusal without sufficient cause in cases of urgency or immediate danger led to the imposition of fines. In some localities, physicians who were not civil servants were required to submit quarterly reports about their activities to the medical authorities. The government also promulgated mandatory fee schedules. In 1869, attempts to create a Reichsgesundheitsamt or Health Office in Prussia that could represent professional interests and administer public health failed. Fortunately for medical professionals, the previous compulsion to provide medical care was canceled in favor of a new free trade ordinance which included Kurierfreiheit (freedom to cure) thus restoring the previously unregulated medical marketplace. While physicians were again exempted from business taxes and allowed to operate according to the laws of supply and demand, the regulations also legally sanctioned all unorthodox healers and quacks to practice their craft (Huerkamp, 1985).

By the 1850s and beyond, health in the traditional middle-class ideology of the "homo hygienicus"—cleanliness and balanced lifestyle—assumed even greater importance in view of the deteriorating health conditions observed in the laboring classes. Could health perhaps become an effective ideology for national integration? But how could this ideal be implemented on a broad scale? How could the life-styles of the masses be standardized? (Labisch, 1985, 1992). For those who adhered to the principles of mercantilism and worked hard to achieve a national unification of Germany, trouble at the base of the social pyramid caused great concern. Sickness was a clear threat to the cohesion and unity of German society. Questions arose concerning the role medicine could play in the face of such threats to the social order. The tactic of promoting the ideology of a universal natural science to achieve scientific and social reforms was not abandoned. Despite efforts to marginalize them, both homeopathy and hydropathy still posed as legitimate alternatives to regular medicine, a reality demonstrated by Wagner's own recourse to water cures in 1850 and again in 1856. In spite of these obstacles, could the scientific physician become the "Führer" to guide the nation toward a productive and healthy life-style?

Working under the banner of an evolving scientific medicine, German physicians founded in 1852 the Verein für gemeinsame Arbeiten zur Förderung der wissenschaftlichen Heilkunde, a professional organization. Although a few famous physicians participated, this association failed to achieve permanent status and eventually dissolved itself in 1869. Professional interests remained low, with some practitioners gradually joining some organizations, largely within governmental, administrative frameworks. The reasons for such a lack of concern were clear. Spurred by the social and economic concerns associated with industrialization, numerous health insurance schemes sprang up in different parts of Germany. As previously envisioned by the 1848 reformers, a growing portion of the population now came into contact with the medical profession, welcoming the expansion of services. Under the various arrangements, practitioners cared for the insured in return for an annual fee. This method became quite popular with less established practitioners, especially recent graduates who considered such "fixed" positions attractive even if the capitation fees were low. Unfortunately, physicians in such plans came under intense scrutiny from the insurance companies' boards of directors, groups intent on keeping the numbers of certified sick members as low as possible even if it required interference with purely therapeutic matters.

THE SOCIAL QUESTION

By the early 1870s, the German medical profession was drawn into contemporary debates about the *soziale Frage* or social question. Concerns about the social and political consequences of industrialization and unfettered capitalism were widely expressed and closely linked to health conditions among the hostile industrial *Lumpenproletariat*. As members of the educated elite, university-educated medical professionals shared the socially conservative outlook considered the standardbearer of German culture. Some played important roles in articulating utopian social and political ideals to bring about such a mythical union of the Volk. Like other *Bildungsbürger*, however, medical professionals in general professed to be apolitical since party activities were beneath their dignity. Instead, they expressed support for a conflict-free society in which all groups and classes worked for the benefit of the whole (Blackbourn and Evans, 1991; Weindling, 1991).

In their perceived role as guardians of the nation's health, physicians were hampered by their relatively modest professional and financial status. Resolutions at the 1869 and 1872 meetings of the Naturforscherversammlungen in Dresden and Leipzig set the stage for the creation in 1873 of a national organization, the Deutsche Aerztever-einsbund (Union of German Medical Associations). This move came in response to perceived contemporary threats to medicine's economic and professional standing, among them strong competition from ho-meopaths, naturopaths, and quacks. Claiming to be a central clearing-house and lobby for professional interests and demands, the Bund immediately launched an aggressive campaign against its nonprofes-sional competitors, trying to stigmatize them as dangerous quacks. In spite of efforts to the contrary, physicians continued to be perceived by the public as private entrepreneurs. Yet, physicians themselves, striving for autonomy and financial independence, saw their activities as incom-patible with the laws of a free market economy (Frevert, 1985).

To rationalize the obvious inequalities of education and health, German thinkers embraced social Darwinism as a proper doctrine of self improvement and progress. Darwin's *The Descent of Man* appeared in 1871, the year of German unification. Like his 1859 *Origin of Species,* Darwin presented an evolutionary view of morphology and physiology that was to profoundly shape subsequent scientific research and public policy. Introduced into Germany by Ernst Haeckel, Darwinism became quite popular and a vehicle for the establishment of social views based on biological analogues. In fact Haeckel's view of society as a highly evolved organism with the imperial government as the central nervous center, promised middle-class Wilhelmine Germans a holistic, biologi-cally grounded Weltanschauung supportive of national unity, order, and hierarchy (Gregory, 1977).

As a professional ideology, Darwinism was also well suited to a de-centralized and competitive university system which encouraged the no-tion that talented and qualified individuals should be rewarded with privilege and influence. Instead of a philosophically oriented Wis-senschaft, Germans now embraced science as the vehicle by which to achieve cultural authority and social status. A veritable obsession with university education ensued aimed at producing further intellectual "mandarins," leaders of an expanding German Kulturstaat. Enrollment soared. Strongly supported by state authorities, the universities became engines of scientific progress, prominently featuring the study of the basic sciences informing medicine. Such research flourished with the infusion of vast sums of tax money to build institutes and laboratories, hire productive scholars and an army of assistants, with little initial con-cern about the utility of such research. As far as the authorities were concerned, this work supported the goals of Germany's cultural superiority and provided students with the essential geistige Bildung as a substitute for the country's diminished political power and colonial imperialism (Shils, 1973).

Medical students exposed to the experimental methods in large laboratories as part of their medical education found such scientific work not only respectable but attractive as a career. In an expanding academic market, many medical graduates thus opted for such academic pursuits. As successful applicants were rewarded with university chairs and laboratory facilities, the scientific enterprise rapidly grew. Of those physicians who completed their research between 1850 and 1859 for the mandatory teaching thesis or Habilitationsschrift, 84 percent received full-time academic appointments. An example of the rapid growth and specialization of the basic sciences in Germany was physiology, originally linked to anatomy. Conscious that this discipline was critical for an understanding of the human organism in health and disease, fifteen new chairs of experimental physiology were established between 1850 to 1864. More than two-thirds of the original contributions made to the field during that time came from German scientists. By 1880, this figure had risen to almost 80 percent (Ben David, 1960). Physicians were convinced that insights obtained from such research would, in time, also improve medical care. The fruits of such research were soon at hand. Aided by the achromatic microscope, Virchow initiated the era of cellular pathology (1859), Schultze defined the protoplasm (1861), Gohnheim discovered the mechanism of inflammation (1864), Helmholtz established physiological optics (1867), Hering and Breuer described the self-regulation of respiration (1868), Fritsch and Hitzig determined the localization of brain functions (1870), while Koch achieved pure cultures of anthrax bacilli (1876) (Temkin, 1959).

While the avalanche of scientific discovery enhanced the prestige of the academic medical profession, ordinary practitioners struggled in an unregulated market where their authority was still contested by lay groups, sectarians, and quacks. Unprotected by state regulations, the new scientific physicians were viewed with suspicion, especially since their therapeutic armamentarium remained circumscribed to traditional measures. The dramatically expanded knowledge of physiology and pathology obtained from laboratory research enhanced diagnostic precision and prognostic accuracy, but so far had failed to produce the expected cures. Even Wagner's so-called erysipelas continued to blossom, frequently interrupting his work, indeed canceling a concert tour in 1880 that would have included San Francisco, "the fulfillment of my boyhood wish" (von Westernhagen, 1978, p. 553).

The German economic crisis of 1878 shattered confidence in social and economic progress and led to a gradual but dramatic change of public opinion. The "Great Depression" lasted for the next two decades, slowing economic growth and triggering successive recessions. In the 1870s, the dislocation caused by rapid urbanization and industrialization only became worse, and was blamed on noninterventionist, laissez-faire liberalism. Bismarck's authoritarian government cracked down hard on labor, causing bitter disputes, strikes, and lockouts. In the eyes of the Bildungsbürgertum, the social organism of Germany had indeed seriously sickened, burdened with an expanding and hostile proletariat beset with problems of venereal disease, infant mortality, alcoholism, crime, prostitution, and mental illness. To flourish, the industrial sector required stringent controls and a collectivist approach to problem solving, not individual piecemeal solutions. Among questions frequently asked was whether certain sectors of the population, the working classes in particular, were suffering from physical and psychological decay. Was such degradation the result of a disregard for the laws of health and heredity?

One approach was to seek the knowledge of science and medicine to improve social conditions. Perhaps biology, broadly interpreted as a natural and social science, could inform policy makers about causes of increased wastage and destruction of human life. Could such biological information be employed to organize and justify new social controls? What could embryology and genetics, physical anthropology and ethnography, nutrition, eugenics, sexual and mental pathology tell us? In 1879, Wagner had forcefully expressed his opposition to experimental science by writing in support of antivivisection, but his efforts were stopped by Virchow. Like many of his compatriots, Wagner resisted the advances of science at the expense of traditional ethics, writing in 1880 that "any science is infected with the taint and therefore with the suspicion of dishonesty and untruthfulness of the masses, so that fantastic dilettantism is summoned forth as a reaction against it (Medicine!)" (Bergfeld, 1980, p. 200).

As the idea took root in Europe and America that biological heredity could be associated with a predisposition to disease, mental competency, criminality, and sexual deviance, a number of theories emerged to explain the link and propose solutions for the elite whose progressive Angst about a possible takeover of Germany by the degenerating but militant proletariat needed to be assuaged. There was hope that Germany's human stock could be revitalized from within according to biological laws and eugenic principles. In the early 1880s the biological sciences gained further prestige through pioneering work in experimental cytology and embryology. Activities in the cell nucleus such as the behavior of chromosomes during fertilization and cell division were meticulously observed with the aid of improved microscopes and dyes. It was soon realized that chromosomes were indeed the carriers of hereditary properties. The impression gained from the research was that an immutable germplasm transmitted by chromosomes from generation to generation was the ultimate source of organic properties, thus weakening all theories about the importance of the environment and acquired traits. In the year of Wagner's fatal heart attack, 1883,[1] the Freiburg biologist August Weissman propounded an idea of the "germ tract" as the hereditary substance continuously passed on and totally unaffected by events occurring during the lifetime of an organism. His biological recasting of Darwinianism became the linchpin of German eugenics (Weindling, 1989b).

In the 1870s and 1880s the degeneration theory formulated by the French psychiatrist Morel in 1857 came to dominate German psychiatric thought. Morel's degeneration hypothesis was based on assumed correlations between nervous diseases and pathological lesions, leading the author to postulate that diseases such as epilepsy, cretinism, hysteria, and other deviant behavior were indeed hereditary, the product of an irreversible physicomental degeneration. Prominent psychiatrists such as Griesinger and Krafft-Ebing welcomed this link between irrationality and biological processes as well as the concept of hereditary predisposition. Krafft-Ebing in his *Psychopathia Sexualis* of 1886 linked sexual perversions with crime and nervous degeneration. The stage was set for an interventionist, eugenic psychiatry that sought to identify the physiological and mental traits of degeneration and remove its victims from society.

In the quest for separating the healthy from the degenerate, authors such as Otto Ammon also looked at racial characteristics by studying military recruits. Ammon supported the idea that the German race

---

[1] Details of his medical condition were provided by his private physician in Venice, Dr. Friedrich Keppler (Dellin, 1983, p. 886).

was threatened by degeneration. In this context a fringe Sozialanthropologie designed to legitimate the ideology of Aryan superiority appeared. Its roots can be traced to the writings of a French aristocrat, Gobineau, who in 1855 had published an essay on *The Inequality of the Human Races.* Gobineau blamed the fall of civilizations on racial mixing. He postulated that only the white race or "Aryans"—especially the Nordic or Germanic subrace, could create a true civilization. Since the other races were decidedly inferior, racial interbreeding necessarily contaminated the purity of blood, leading to degeneration. Gobineau's ideas, based on dubious historical and linguistic arguments, failed to receive attention in his homeland. Some of his followers, however, reinterpreted the racist tenets, linking them to biological criteria, including Weissman's theory of the germplasm. Gobineau first met Wagner in 1876, and the Aryan supremacy thesis found ready supporters among members of the Bayreuth circle (Weindling, 1989a).

The early 1880s viewed medicine as a surrogate for the state, extending its domain over new areas such as sexuality, social hygiene, and mental health, ultimately providing scientific solutions to the state's problems. Social deviancy had to be medicalized and its victims controlled through procedures and institutions developed in part by medicine with governmental approval and support. This began when the 1883 Sickness Insurance and the 1884 Industrial Accident Acts were passed. This state intervention in the area of health insurance brought a rising percentage of the population into medical offices. From the very beginning, the new opportunities for medical care forced workers to seek it even when they were not in the habit of consulting professionals, dramatically increasing the frequency of sicknesses seen at the German Krankenkassen. Contact with lower-class workers forged anonymous and limited healing relationships, except among a handful of idealistic, socially committed physicians who went beyond narrow treatments to provide health information. Instead of addressing obvious issues of material conditions which affected the health of working populations, most medical practitioners employed by the funds narrowed their focus to the "medical" level of their patients' problems, concentrating on medication and possible admission to hospitals.

Germany was unique in developing such a medicalization scheme with state support. The medical profession was not consulted, nor did it oppose the sickness insurance bill. Practitioners correctly foresaw an improvement in their economic situation, since henceforth a portion of their charity practice was to be reimbursed. Moreover, forcing workers to consult physicians who had to validate sickness would inevitably lead to an erosion of traditional patterns of self and domestic care while also weakening the competing lay systems of healing. The new social legislation, however, failed to include regulations governing the relationships between the sickness funds and physicians, thus creating a host of problems. Insurance regulations granted company physicians a central position of absolute authority over the workers, with draconian penalties for those who failed to obey. Discovery and reporting of malingerers, demands for certified medical excuses from work, evaluation of work-related disabilities, restrictions on expensive prescriptions, posed tough ethical problems for practitioners working for the insurance funds. Caregiving was limited to certain physicians approved by the insurance company, many of whom abused the system by increasing their practices and income (Kater, 1985).

The rise of scientific medicine during the last quarter of the century conferred an unprecedented level of cultural recognition on the medical profession, particularly academic physicians who enjoyed a high measure of prestige as civil servants. Medical students exposed to the experimental methods in large laboratories found such scientific work not only respectable but attractive as a full-time career. In an expanding academic market, growing numbers of graduates opted for academic pursuits as successful applicants were rewarded with university chairs and laboratories. Attracted by the promise of higher status and more lucrative practices, medical specialists flourished in the private sector. While the avalanche of scientific discovery enhanced the prestige of academics, ordinary practitioners continued to struggle in an unregulated market where their authority was contested by lay groups and sectarians. Unprotected by state regulations, these new scientific physicians were viewed with considerable suspicion, especially since their therapeutic weapons remained circumscribed to traditional measures (Jarausch, 1982).

Indeed, the dramatically expanded knowledge of physiology and pathology obtained from laboratory research obviously enhanced diagnostic precision and prognostic accuracy, but failed to produce expected cures. As competition stiffened, and the number of young physicians soared, German physicians experienced increasing difficulties in maintaining middle-class living standards. Between 1889 and 1898 the population grew by 11.5 percent while physicians increased by 56.2 percent.

Nevertheless, the scientific and institutional contexts of the Krankenkassen's formation allowed for the establishment of larger, laboratory-based clinics within which member physicians located their offices. As the traditional relationship faded, the public responded by becoming more critical and less trusting.

EPILOGUE

As self-appointed custodians of the nation's health, German physicians in the 1880s proposed three main directions of research and public policy to lighten the country's health problems. They pledged to examine the social factors involved in the creation of disease, to develop the sciences of bacteriology, serology, and immunology in the fight against infectious diseases, and to explore the role of heredity in the etiology of disease. The latter promised medical solutions to Germany's social questions, especially regarding problems seen by neurologists and psychiatrists which suggested hereditary predispositions to physical and psychological decay. Such a program converted medicine into a de facto instrument of the state, expanding its domain over new areas such as sexuality, social hygiene, and mental health.

By 1890, German medicine stood at the crossroads of conflicting ideologies of health and professional agendas. Confronted with growing numbers of individuals suffering from diseases of industrialization and poverty, physicians working for insurance companies could label many illnesses "constitutional" or "degenerative," implying that they were the result of inherited traits, thus shifting blame for the health problem to the patients themselves. An alternative option was to take a preventative approach and provide the necessary eugenic advice to forestall the appearance of degenerative diseases in the first place. Addressing these issues was one prominent medical author, Friedrich W. Schallmayer. His influential 1891 treatise *Concerning the Imminent Physical Degeneration of Civilized Humanity and the Nationalization of the Medical Profession* sought to extend Darwin and Galton's views that social progress could only occur through the physical and mental improvement of a population. It was imperative to establish a rational management of human reproduction—a racial hygiene to ensure the propagation of an adequate number of "fit" individuals necessary for the survival of European civilization (Weiss, 1986).

"Fitness" was to a great extent defined in biomedical terms, including proper heredity and physical constitution. In proposing such a solution, Schallmayer actually viewed contemporary scientific medicine as an obstacle to eugenic goals, since it tampered with natural selection by extending the life span of "defectively constituted" or "generally weak" individuals. Here Schallmayer, who had spent his 1884 internship in a psychiatric clinic, wholeheartedly followed the ideas of the German degeneration theorists. The average nervous system was incapable of keeping up with the fast pace of industrialized society. To compound matters, psychiatrists protected mental defectives in asylums, actually releasing some who could then propagate their defective genetic heritage. But there were other undesirable groups hindering the collective efficiency of the German Reich as, for example, those suffering from tuberculosis. In Schallmayer's view, this disease had "cleansed humanity of a considerable portion of its weakest members" (Weiss, 1987a, p. 46).

To assist in such a rational program of patient selection, German physicians had to become de facto agents of the state, recording and codifying the nation's stock of pathological traits. Each citizen would be issued an official Krankenpasskarte, a sort of health identification card containing information about previous diseases believed to reveal significant hereditary traits. If empowered to function as true guardians of the empire's health, moreover, medical professionals needed financial and social protection from patients and insurance companies. "As I see it," wrote Schallmeyer, "this requires the transformation of the entire medical profession into a class of civil servants" (Weiss, 1987a, p. 59). Thus, physicians such as Schallmeyer in 1891 proposed that the medical profession be incorporated into a separate category within the traditional German Beamtenstand that promised material security and high social position.

At the core of these suggestions remained the perennial tensions observed by Wagner throughout his lifetime between medicine as a Gewerbstätigkeit or commercial venture and the traditional ethical concept of physicianhood or Standesehre seemingly compromised by the Krankenkassen practice. Indeed, by the 1890s, medical practitioners realized that the expanding sickness insurance funds increasingly imposed their own power on the medical profession, forcing on them greater patient loads and the prescription of cheaper drugs, all detrimental to quality care and the image of the doctor. A new impersonality based on scientific objectivity also affected patient–physician relationships, indirectly providing traditional fringe healing practices with new customers (Risse, 1982). In the end, however, Schallmeyer's ideas went unheeded. The profession remained independent, subjected to the marketplace forces of a capitalist society. Yet, the concept of a greater social good overriding the individual goals of patients persisted and was to play a most nefarious role during the Third German Reich.

REFERENCES

Ackerknecht, E. H. (1932), Beiträge zur Geschichte der Medizinalreform von 1848. *Sudhoffs Arch.*, 25:61–109; 112–183.

———— (1953), *Rudolf Virchow: Doctor, Statesman, Anthropologist.* Madison: University of Wisconsin Press.

Anderson, R. (1980), *Wagner, a Biography.* London: C. Bingley.

Ben David, E. G. J. (1960), Scientific productivity and academic organization in 19th century medicine. *Amer. Sociol. Rev.*, 25:828–843.

Bergfeld, J., Ed. (1980), *The Diary of Richard Wagner, 1865–1882.* New York: Cambridge University Press.

Blackbourn, D., & Eley, G. (1984), *The Peculiarities of German History. Bourgeois Society and Politics in Nineteenth-Century Germany,* Oxford: Oxford University Press.

———— Evans, R. J., Eds. (1991), *The German Bourgeoisie. Essays on the Social History of the German Middle Class.* London: Routledge.

Bleker, J. (1983), Between romantic and scientific medicine: Johann Lukas Schoenlein and the natural history school, 1825–1845. *Clio Medica,* 18:191–201.

———— (1988), Biedermeiermedizin-Medizin der Biedermeier? Tendenzen, Probleme, Widersprüche, 1830–1850, *Medizinhist. J.,* 23:5–22.

Broman, T. (1989), University reform in medical thought at the end of the eighteenth century. *Osiris,* 5:36–53.

Cranefield, P. F. (1966), The philosophical and cultural interests of the biophysics movement of 1847. *J. Hist. Med.,* 12:1–7.

Darwin, C. (1859), *Origin of Species by Means of Natural Selection.* London: J. Murray.

———— (1871), *The Descent of Man and Selection of Relation to Sex.* London: J. Murray.

Dellin, M. (1983), *Richard Wagner, sein Leben, sein Jahrhundert.* Munich, Germany: Piper.

Frevert, U. (1985), Professional medicine and the working classes in Imperial Germany. *J. Contemp. Hist.,* 20:637–658.

Gobineau, A. (1855), *The Inequality of the Human Races,* tr. A. Collins. London: Heinemann, 1915.

Gregory, F. (1977), *Scientific Materialism in Nineteenth-Century Germany.* Dordrecht, Holland: Reidel.

Heischkel Artelt, E. (1967), Die Welt des praktischen Arztes im 19. Jahrhundert. In: *Der Arzt und der Kranke in der Gesellschaft des 19. Jahrhunderts,* ed. W. Altelt & W. Ruegg. Stuttgart, Germany: F. Enke, pp. 1–16.

Huerkamp, C. (1985), *Der Aufstieg der Aerzte im 19. Jahrhundert.* Göttingen, Germany: Vandernhoeck & Ruprecht.

——— (1990), The making of the modern medical profession, 1800–1914: Prussian doctors in the 19th century. In: *German Professions, 1800–1950,* ed. G. Cocks & K. H. Jarausch. New York: Oxford University Press, pp. 66–84.

Jarausch, K. H. (1982), *Students, Society, and Politics in Imperial Germany.* Princeton, NJ: Princeton University Press.

Kater, M. H. (1985), Professionalization and socialization of physicians in Wilhelmine and Weimar Germany. *J. Contemp. Hist.,* 20:677–701.

Krafft-Ebing, R. von (1886), *Psychopathia Sexualis; A Medico-forensic Study,* tr. H. E. Wedeck. New York: Putnam, 1965.

Labisch, A. (1985), Doctors, workers, and the scientific cosmology of the industrial world: The social construction of "health" and the "homo hygienicus." *J. Contemp. Hist.,* 20:599–615.

——— (1992), *Homo Hygienicus, Gesundheit und Medizin in der Neuzeit.* Frankfurt, Germany: Campus Verlag.

Osler, W. (1884), Notes of a visit to European medical centers. *Arch. Med.,* 12:170.

Paul, R. (1984), German academic science and the mandarin ethos, 1850–1880. *Brit. J. Hist. Sci.,* 17:1–29.

Richter, H. E. (1873), *Aerztliches Vereinsblatt,* 9/10:56.

Risse, G. B. (1982), Patients and their healers: Historical studies in health care. In: *Who Decides? Conflicts of Rights in Health Care,* ed. N. K. Bell. Clifton, NJ: Humana Press, pp. 27–45.

Schallmayer, F. W. (1891), *Vererbung und Auslese in ihren Soziologischen und politischen Bedeutung,* 2nd ed. Jena: G. Fischer, 1910.

Shils, E. (1973), The power of the state and the dignity of academic calling in Imperial Germany. *Minerva,* 9:571–632.

Temkin, O. (1959), The dependence of medicine upon basic scientific thought. In: *The Historical Development of Physiological Thought,* ed. C. McBrooks & P. F. Cranefield. New York: Hafner, 1959, pp. 5–21.

Virchow, R. (1859), *Disease, Life, and Man: Selected Essays,* tr. L. J. Rather. Stanford, CA: Stanford University Press, 1958.

Weindling, P. (1989a), *Health, Race, and German Politics between National Unification and Nazism, 1870–1945.* New York: Cambridge University Press.

——— (1989b), The *Sonderweg* of German eugenics: Nationalism and scientific internationalism. *Brit. J. Hist. Sci.,* 22:321–333.

——— (1991), Bourgeois values, doctors and the state: The professionalization of medicine in German 1848–1933. In: *The German Bourgeoisie,* ed. D. Blackbourn, & R. J. Evans. London: Routledge, pp. 198–223.

Weiss, S. F. (1986), Wilhelm Schallmeyer and the logic of German eugenics. *Isis*, 77:33–46.

—— (1987a), *Race Hygiene and National Efficiency*. Berkeley: University of California Press.

—— (1987b), The race hygiene movement in Germany. *Osiris*, 3:193–236.

Westernhagen, von R. (1978), *Wagner, a Biography*, Vol. 2, tr. M. Whittall. Cambridge, U.K.: Cambridge University Press.

9

The Impact of Richard Wagner on Adolf Hitler

Fritz C. Redlich, M.D.

The Hitler biographer Hans Jürgen Eitner (1981) wrote: "There is much Hitler in Wagner" (pp. 122–133). While my knowledge of Richard Wagner is too limited to allow me to deliberate on this topic, I feel qualified to discuss the question, "How much Wagner is in Hitler?" While Borchmeyer (1984) and the museum director Eger (1985) both minimized Wagner's impact on Hitler, Gutman (1968) and Zelinski (1988, 1989) found it prominent. Zelinski (1983) in particular pointed to the considerable public relations effort after the end of World War II on the part of the Bayreuth establishment to "denazify" Wagner and his family. While the well-known Hitler biographer Maser (1983) barely mentioned Wagner's name, Waite (1977) stated that, "it is very difficult to exaggerate the importance of Wagner in Hitler's life and thought" (p. 103). My own perception is close to Waite's point of view.

Hitler had two important historical models, the Prussian King Frederick the Great and Richard Wagner. He considered himself, Frederick the Great, and Richard Wagner to be the greatest Germans. In contrast to his feelings about his own father, Hitler felt no ambivalence about Wagner, but only admiration. In an obsequious letter to Richard Wagner's son Siegfried, Hitler (1924) stated that Siegfried's "father of blessed memory" (hochselige Herr Vater) had supplied the spiritual sword for national socialism. What was it in Wagner's life and work that impressed Hitler so profoundly?

A BRIEF CHRONOLOGY OF ADOLF HITLER'S INVOLVEMENT
WITH RICHARD WAGNER'S LIFE AND MUSIC

Adolf Hitler was thirteen years old when he first encountered Wagner's operas. In *Mein Kampf* (1925), he wrote about his boundless enthusiasm upon seeing *Lohengrin* at the Linz Theater (p. 17). After that, he saw nearly all of Wagner's operas, some of them many times. According to August Kubizek (1966), a music student and companion of Hitler's youth, Hitler attended forty performances of *Tristan and Isolde* and considered it Wagner's greatest opus (pp. 88–98). The two youngsters rarely saw the end of a Wagner opera at the Hofoper in Vienna because they had to get home before ten o'clock in order to avoid paying the janitor to open the door. Not the most reliable reporter, Kubizek also stated that he and the young Hitler attended a performance of Wagner's early opera *Rienzi*, the story of a Roman tribune fighting for freedom and justice for his people. After this performance, Hitler reportedly was in a state of ecstasy and swore that some day he would liberate the German people. Thirty-two years later, when Kubizek repeated the story to Hitler in Bayreuth, Hitler is reputed to have said, "This was the beginning" (p. 330). True or not, it is a good anecdote for the Hitler myth.

In another chapter, Kubizek described how Hitler tried to compose an opera based on a libretto that Wagner did not use. In the libretto, *Wieland der Schmied*, full of murder and deceit, Wieland, a blacksmith with iron swan wings, is mistreated and enslaved by his king, and avenges himself (quite likely an allusion to Hitler's father). Hitler knew nothing about composition, but he was able to hack out some melodies on the piano that Kubizek had to write down in musical notation. Naturally, this unrealistic effort—not uncharacteristic for the young Hitler—led to nothing (p. 231). According to Kubizek, Hitler was thoroughly familiar with Wagner's writings and could quote his letters by heart. However, neither what Hitler read as an adolescent nor what he read later is known, though it is very probable that he read two Wagner treatises on Jewish music (Wagner, pp. 66–85). Although he did not mention these treatises specifically, Hitler (April, 4, 1942) made degrading remarks about the "banker Meyerbeer" in his monologues (p. 224), just as Wagner did in the article when he mentioned Meyerbeer and "Jewish" music. Eventually, Hitler's anti-Semitism clearly extended to music, although it is not certain whether he already harbored these sentiments in Vienna. Kubizek (1966) stated that Hitler liked Felix Mendelssohn-Bartholdy and admired Gustav Mahler, then director of the Vienna Hofoper (p. 231). However, Hitler reportedly reminisced that he once got furious when he left a performance of *Götterdämmerung* and passed some Jews with Yiddish accents ("mauschelnde Juden"), remarking that there could be no greater contrast than between them and Wagner's divine music (p. 231).

Hitler's enthusiasm for Wagner, never dormant, became stronger under the influence of associates in Munich after the First World War. Most important amongst these individuals was Dietrich Eckhart, a journalist and author who at one time had been a theater critic in Bayreuth. Eckhart cared little for music but admired Wagner. Other prominent Wagnerites who were in close contact with both Hitler and the Wagner family included an early supporter, the musical Ernst Hanfstaengl, who entertained Hitler by playing Wagnerian melodies for him; Frau Helene Bechstein, wife of the piano manufacturer; and Hans Frank, the future governor of the General Government in Poland who was sentenced to death for his crimes against humanity. In 1923 Hitler fulfilled his ardent desire to visit Wahnfried for the first time; he was to return on many occasions. He felt comfortable with the members of the Wagner family and used the familiar *"Du"* with them. With some reservations, Hitler especially liked Richard Wagner's son Siegfried, an opportunistic fellow traveler who saw advantages for Bayreuth in a close friendship with Adolf Hitler, although he maintained the "Jewish connection" until 1933.

After Siegfried's death, his English-born wife Winifred became the new *"Herrin* of Bayreuth." An early member of the National Socialist Party (1922), Winifred Wagner admired and liked Hitler who returned her feelings. After the war, Winifred Wagner was sentenced to 450 days' labor for her national socialist activities. In a lengthy interview filmed by Seyberberg in 1974, she still spoke of Hitler as good, kind, and charming. About the darker side of Hitler she said she knew nothing (*Der Spiegel,* 1975)—she also commented that this was none of her business!

A very important person who conveyed his impression of Richard Wagner to Hitler was Houston Stewart Chamberlain, a British philosopher who had lived in Germany and married one of Wagner's daughters, Eva. Undoubtedly Hitler was familiar with Chamberlain's anti-Semitic opus, *Grundlagen des Zwanzigsten Jahrhunderts* (1932), as well as with his biography of Richard Wagner, which Hitler had in his library. In a letter, Chamberlain (1926) addressed and celebrated Hitler as the Führer and

Savior of Germany. By 1924, Hitler was in close and permanent contact with the Wagner family, though for a while the relations were strained. He stated in one of his monologues that he was infuriated that Friedrich Schorr, a Jew, and a famous Helden baritone, had sung Wotan. He termed it a racial disgrace (Rassenschande) and refused to return to Bayreuth for years, despite numerous pleading letters and telephone calls from Winifred Wagner. After he came to power, Hitler made Bayreuth a national shrine to Wagner, to serve the German people. A second Wagner shrine was Nuremberg, the site of National Party Meetings (Reichsparteitage), where performances of *Die Meistersinger* crowned these huge assemblies. The third designated Wagner City was Munich, the "capital of the movement." The annual Bayreuth festivals continued well into the war, until all theaters were closed. From 1933 on, complete harmony existed between Hitler and members of the Wagner family. The only exception was Richard Wagner's granddaughter Friedelind, who, under the influence of Arturo Toscanini, denounced national socialism, and emigrated from Germany (Fest, 1985).

SIMILARITIES BETWEEN WAGNER'S AND HITLER'S LIFE HISTORIES

Striking similarities in the life histories of Wagner and Hitler have been noted by biographers Eitner (1981) and Fest (1985), and by the psychohistorian Waite (1977). The paternity of both Wagner and Hitler has remained obscure, and both were concerned that they may have had Jewish ancestors, although no objective evidence for such descent in either Wagner or Hitler has been established. As children Wagner and Hitler were both surrounded by doting females, and both had a strong attachment to their mothers, manifested in unrecognized dependency needs and insatiable demands for love. Both believed that women were destined to remain in serving roles. The two men's early experiences differed in that Hitler was abused and humiliated as a child, whereas Wagner was not. In Hitler as well as in Wagner, passive needs were camouflaged by an outward display of aggressive masculinity. Both had stormy periods during puberty and adolescence. Both had learning difficulties, acquiring their vast knowledge in an autodidactic manner, and were inclined to regard school knowledge with contempt. Both rebelled against authority and fought for what they considered social justice. In

Hitler's rebellion one can discern strong frustration over not being recognized by his father. Gutman (1968) characterized Wagner as having a need to command and demand, and this description also fits Hitler. As men, both Wagner and Hitler were extraordinarily intense, stormy in their relationships, and inclined to explosive rages and lasting anger, resentment, and hostility. They talked incessantly and overwhelmed both their companions and their opponents with words. They easily suspected enemies and, if these did not exist, they created them. Both were inclined to be suspicious and paranoid and responded to real and imaginary humiliations with great animosity.

Both Wagner and Hitler were dramatic, theatrical personalities, at times exhibiting what clinically could be labeled hysterical behavior. Both were extremely intense and self-centered. A similarity in their monetary practices also is worth noting: both incurred debts without the slightest inhibition and spent money without restraint. However, while Wagner was outright greedy, Hitler was relatively unconcerned about personal possessions. Both were vegetarians—Wagner was a radical antivivisectionist, and Hitler an ardent lover of animals. Both suffered from insomnia as well as frequent brief periods of depression from which they readily recovered on their own. Hitler and Wagner both talked of suicide in tight situations.

One significant difference between the two men is that Wagner established close mutual relationships—although one of his most important relationships, with Friedrich Nietzsche, collapsed when Nietzsche criticized him (Nietzsche, 1889). Hitler, on the other hand, never had any close friends, except for the passive and admiring Kubizek. Although both Wagner and Hitler used women for their own purposes, the most striking difference between the two is that Wagner had a rich love life. Hitler's was frustrated and unhappy, and in the monologues he expressed envy that Wagner, in contrast to himself, had been able to find women who understood him. In the later periods of their lives, however, both men claimed to have overcome their sensuality.

Hitler's identification with Wagner is illustrated by a statement he made in his final plea during the Hitler trial in 1924:

> When I stood for the first time at Wagner's tomb, my heart flowed over with pride that under the tombstone rested a man who forbade it to be written . . . here rests the secret counsellor, music director, his Excellency Baron Richard Wagner. Already then I was proud

and happy that this man, like many before in Germany's history, renounced taking a title just to preserve his name before posterity. It was not out of modesty that I wanted to be the drummer (of the movement), but because this is the highest. Everything else is a bagatelle.

The far-reaching identification of Hitler with Wagner is impressive, yet differences also are noteworthy. Hitler regarded himself as a politician-artist. Admirers such as Winifred Wagner, Hitler's architect Hermann Giesler (1977), and Hans Severus Ziegler (1946), music director for the Reich, emphasized that Hitler was essentially an artist—"ein musischer Mensch." It is undeniable that Hitler had a great interest in the arts and was, in his domineering way, not insensitive to many artistic issues. He was, however, primarily a politician, while Wagner was primarily an artist who believed that humanity could be served through art. In his identification with Wagner, Hitler discounted the human weaknesses that came to his attention, such as Wagner's craving for luxuries, silk, and velvet, and his effeminate traits (Domarus, 1924, p. 200). He excused Wagner's litigious and paranoid tendencies, so similar to his own, and believed that Wagner had been unjustly persecuted by the Jewish press. Hitler saw in Wagner what he wanted to see in him: a genius who believed in German supremacy and victory over racial inferiors. He viewed himself as the protector and executioner of Wagnerian thought. Regardless of what Wagner had in mind, Hitler wanted to be more Wagnerian than Wagner. Fest (1985) summarized Wagner's impact in the following way: "This strange brew compounded of bloody vapors, dragon slaying, mania for domination, treachery, sexual elitism, paganism and ultimately salvation and tolling bells on a theatrical Good Friday, were a perfect ideological match for Hitler's anxieties and needs" (p. 56).

THE IMPACT OF WAGNER'S IDEAS ON HITLER'S WORLDVIEW

Before any consideration of the relationship between Hitler's ideology and that of Wagner, it should be kept in mind that Hitler truly loved Wagner's music and dramas. As a "Wagnerian," Hitler found himself in very distinguished company, amongst the greatest minds of our times, including James Joyce, Bernard Shaw, and Thomas Mann. No one can object to the fact that Hitler loved Wagner's music, or even to the fact that he put Wagner's work above all other music. This is a matter of taste. Actually, Hitler's musical taste was not so exclusive; he also liked the music of Johann Strauss and Franz Lehár, yet it was "Wagner, Wagner über Alles." What aroused Hitler was the ecstatic and intoxicating nature of Wagner's music, the fact that it was heroic and German. In his youth, Hitler was fascinated with German mythology. Although he later disavowed "folkish" statements about German mythology, in Wagner's operas he accepted German hero worship. The themes of Wagner's great operas—particularly the *Ring, Lohengrin, Parsifal,* and *Tristan*—were deeply meaningful for him. To analyze in depth Hitler's understanding and misunderstanding of Wagnerian themes would be a worthwhile task for an understanding of Hitler.[1] It can be assumed that Hitler empathized with many Wagnerian characters: with the young heroic Siegfried, a victim of dark forces; with the proud German artists Walther von Stolzing and Hans Sachs; with the secret-bearer Lohengrin; and with the purity of Parsifal, the founder of a new Germanic religion. In a spirited article, Carl Gustav Jung (1936) described the archetype of the German storm god Wotan as a subject of identification for Hitler. Less acceptable is Hitler's downgrading of other national music. In the monologues (February 22/23, 1942), Hitler stated, "You can imagine Verdi played by an organ grinder, but not Wagner." For Hitler, Wagner's music and drama were sublime.

More troublesome are parallels between the ideologies of the two men. The anti-Semitism of both was radical and particularly ugly. Both were elitists and believed in the supremacy of extremely gifted and unique individuals over the masses. Both had similar ideas about social justice and viewed themselves as revolutionaries. However, Hitler's anti-Semitism was consistent and murderous. The otherwise ambivalent Führer never relented on this issue until his final hateful statement in his political testament (Hitler, 1945). On the other hand, Wagner's anti-Semitism was inconsistent, and, unlike Hitler, he cannot be charged with murder.

Wagner maintained friendships with a number of Jewish admirers—the first Parsifal conductor, Hermann Levy, as well as Josef Rubinstein, Karl Taussig, and others. He had a long-lasting love affair with

---

[2] Hartmut Zelinski has begun to tackle this task, although he focuses on Wagner rather than on Hitler.

the singer Judith Gautier and daughter of the Jewish singer Giulia Gris. Yet reasons for linking him to the Holocaust go back to some much-quoted remarks. One of them, made at the end of the paper on Jewish music, reads, "Bear in mind there is but one redemption from the curse weighing upon you—the redemption of Ahasversus, the cataclysm." What did he mean? Like Hitler, Wagner did not believe that religious conversion or intermarriage could solve what he regarded as the "Jewish problem." Did he imply that the "Jewish problem" was insoluble and that suicide was the only solution—such as in the case of the Jewish philosopher Otto Weininger, an ardent admirer of Richard Wagner, and Wagner's young friend Taussig? There are more incriminating remarks. Cosima Wagner (1976) wrote in her diary that Richard, after a performance of *Nathan der Weise* and the Ring Theater fire in Vienna, said that all Jews in the theater should burn to death and that the fact that 416 "Israelites" died in the disaster did not increase his sympathy (July 17 and 18, 1881). Wagner called this a joke, but what a joke! Another remark reported by Cosima stated that Richard believed in the deportation (Ausweisung) of all Jews from Germany. In the thirties, Hitler also spoke of deportation, one step along "the twisted road to Auschwitz" (Schleunes, 1970).

Waite maintained that Wagner's heroic stature was related to Hitler's elitist view of the Führer principle. Granted, a relationship between hero worship and dictatorial rule exists. Both men viewed themselves as revolutionaries. Wagner's revolutionary role in music is uncontested. Both Hitler's and Wagner's roles as political revolutionaries, however, are ambiguous. Hitler intended to be an agent of change, but actually, by his own admission, he was not radical enough. And Wagner's role, with his sycophantic affection for the mad Bavarian King Ludwig II, also is not compatible with the role of a true revolutionary. Both men claimed that they strived for justice, and some early torts may well have shaped both men. Hitler's concept of justice was the unrestricted right and rule of the strong over the weak. The most important difference between Hitler and Wagner was that Hitler, although he viewed himself as an artist-politician, was in fact a politician, and foremost a destructive politician. Wagner wanted redemption of the world, so he preached, through love and art.

Can we really assume that Hitler's ideology came principally from Wagner? I believe that Hitler's destructive social Darwinism can be traced to many intellectual, political, and deeply personal sources. His anti-Semitism can be traced as easily to Theodor Fritsch, author of the *Handbuch des Judentums*, which Hitler read in Vienna before 1913, and to the teachings of Eckhart (1925) after the end of World War I in 1919, as well as to Wagner's essays. Hitler's anti-Semitism can also be explained as an expression of political expedience, when he recognized in 1919 that the Germans were deeply troubled over their defeat and the Treaty of Versailles, and wanted a scapegoat. Finally, it also can be traced to deeply personal matters. Both men were obsessed with the idea that they might have had a Jewish ancestor, and both held the idea that Jewry was evil and produced degeneration and destruction. Waite added another important suggestion. Hitler was deeply aroused by Wagner's treatment of the topic of incest. Incestuous relationships in his family, within his own generation as well as in previous generations, were deeply troublesome to Hitler. The mere fact that Wagner dealt with this topic must have been liberating for Hitler. No specific citation by Hitler about this is known, but undoubtedly Hitler was aware of Wagner's text in *Die Walküre.*

Fricka: *Blutschande entblüht dem Bunde eines Zwillingspaars. Mir schauert das Herz, es schwindelt mein Hirn; bräutlich umfing die Schwester der Bruder. Wann ward es erlebt, daß leiblich Geschwister sich liebten?* Wotan: *Heut has Du's erlebt* [Act I, Scene 1].

[Freely translated in the English *Walküre* score:

Fricka: Foul shame doth spring from the bond of a twinborn pair. I shudder at heart, my reason doth reel; took for his bride the brother the sister. Whenever was it known that brother and sister were lovers.
Wotan: Now it is known to thee.]

WAGNER'S MUSIC AND ANTI-SEMITISM

In a challenging article, citing a most obsequious letter by Wagner, Zelinski raises the question: How anti-Semitic can a great composer be? Wagner was more than a great composer—he was also a dramatist and philosopher—and this makes the issue complicated. If Brahms or Chopin had been radical anti-Semites, one could still enjoy their music without much conflict. In Wagner, this is more difficult because he was the creator of musical dramas. Let me shift for a moment to another man, considered by most a genius: Pablo Picasso. Picasso was generally regarded as a rather nasty person—yet should this be a reason not to acknowledge or admire his art, and not to consider him a genius if one is so inclined? Let me point to two extreme responses to Wagner and his worldview. One is the response of Thomas Mann, who considered Wagner a genius. Thomas Mann was thoroughly familiar with Wagner's thoughts and also was an irreconcilable enemy of national socialism. In two lectures—one given immediately after Hitler seized power in Munich in March, 1933 (Mann, 1935), and the other given in Zurich in 1937 (Mann, 1945)—he expressed his admiration for Wagner's artistic genius. The other extreme point of view is represented by Wagner's reception in Israel. Until now, Wagner has not been performed in Israel, and attempts at performing his work have been met with riotous protests. With respect to this issue, I side with Thomas Mann. One encouraging development in Israel is the appearance of a book in Hebrew with the intriguing title *Who Is Afraid of Richard Wagner?* in which the musicologist Benzin Orgad (cited by Eger, 1985) stated that Wagner is not a symbol of the Holocaust. In this respect he is insignificant. His greatness is in his music.

Seyberberg in his great film *Winifred Wagner and Wahnfried* (1974) depicts the demon Hitler rising from Wagner's tomb. However, in my view, the demon rose from German soil, conjured by a large number of Germans at a unique juncture in history. Hitler was aided and ultimately destroyed by a large segment of the world. The forces of life and love were stronger than the forces of death and hatred. Richard Wagner understood these forces and, strangely enough, another genius, as different from Wagner or Hitler as one could be, understood them, too: Sigmund Freud. I think that, to understand Hitler and Wagner, one must understand Freud, as well as Jung and Adler—and even if one does, much mystery remains.

REFERENCES

Borchmeyer, D. (1984), *Das Theater Richard Wagners.*
Chamberlain, H. S. (1926), Letter to Adolf Hitler. *Illustrierter Beobachter,* 2:6.
———— (1932), *Die Grundlagen des Zwanzigsten Jahrhunderts.* Munich.
Domarus, (1924), *Hitler Prozess.* Munich, 1928.

Eckhart, D. (1925), *Der Bolschewismus von Moses bis Lenin.* Munich.

Eger, M. (1985), *Richard Wagner und die Juden.* Bayreuth.

Eitner, H. J. (1981), *Der Führer.* Munich.

Fest, J. (1985), *Hitler,* tr. R. & C. Winston. New York.

Giesler, H. (1977), *Ein anderer Hitler.* Leoni.

Gutman, R. W. (1968), *Richard Wagner.* New York.

Hitler, A. (1924), Letter to Siegfried Wagner, 5 May 1924. In: *Adolf Hitler: Sämtliche Aufzeichnungen,* ed. E Jäckel & A. Kuhn. Stuttgart: 1980, pp. 1231–1233.

—— (1925), *Mein Kampf,* tr. R. Manheim. Boston, 1943.

—— (1942), *Monologe im Führerhauptquartier,* ed. W. Jochmann. Hamburg, 1980.

—— (1945), Political testament. In: *Nuremberg Documents.*

—— (1959), Bormann documents. In: *Testaments Politiques.* Paris.

Jung, C. G. (1936), Wotan. *Neue Schweizer Rundschau,* III: 657–669.

Kubizek, A. (1966), *Adolf Hitler, mein Jugend Freund.* Graz.

Mann, T. (1935), Leiden und Grösse Richard Wagners. In: *Leiden und Grösse der Meister.* Berlin, pp. 87–163.

—— (1945), Leiden und Grösse Richard Wagners. In: *Adel des Geistes.* Stockholm, pp. 398–472.

Maser, W. (1983), *Adolf Hitler,* 8th ed. Munich.

Nietzsche, F. (1889a), *Der Fall Wagner.* In: *Gesammelte Werke.* Berlin, 1969.

—— (1889b), *Gesamt Ausgabe (Collected Papers),* Vol. 3. Berlin, 1969.

Schleunes, K. (1970). *The Twisted Road to Auschwitz.* Urbana, IL. *Der Spiegel* (1975), 31:84–86.

Wagner, C. (1976), *Tagebücher.* Munich.

Wagner, R. (1871–1885), *Gesammelte Werke (Complete Works),* Volume 5. Leipzig.

Waite, R. L. (1977), *The Psychopathic God, Adolf Hitler.* New York.

Zelinski, H. (1978), *Die Feuerkur des Richard Wagner oder die neue Religion durch Vernichtung.*

—— (1983), Das erschreckende Erwachen und wie man Wagner von Hitler befreit. *Neue Zeitschrift für Musik,* 9–16, Hamburg.

—— (1988), Der Dirigent Hermann Levi. In: *Geschichte und Kultur der Juden in Bayern,* ed. M. Treml & J. Kirmeier. Munich, pp. 411–424.

—— (1989), Lösung Siegfried. In: *Den Trümmern der eigenen Welt,* ed. U. Bernbach. Hamburg, pp. 201–249.

Ziegler, H. S. (1946), *Hitler aus dem Erleben dargestellt.* Göttingen.

10

Sickness or Redemption? Wagnerism and the Consequences

Thomas S. Grey, Ph.D.

DER FALL NIETZSCHE

Shortly before succumbing to the debilitating physical paralysis and mental illness that put an end to his career (and eventually, his life), Friedrich Nietzsche published his scathing attack on the one-time idol of his youth: Richard Wagner. "And here I begin in earnest," writes Nietzsche in section 5 of *The Case of Wagner*. "Far be it from me to look on helplessly while this decadent corrupts our health—and music as well. Is Wagner a human being at all? Isn't he rather a sickness? He makes sick whatever he touches—*he has made music sick*" (Nietzsche, 1888b, p. 164).

One could probably chart a fairly close correlation between the severely declining state of Nietzsche's own health since the late 1870s and his increasing alienation from Wagner.[1] Doubtless the bilious vituperation of the later writings on Wagner have much to do with personal and psychological themes in Nietzsche's biography. Yet he is only the most prominent (and by no means the first) exponent of a "pathological" metaphor—a recurrent trope throughout much turn-of-the-century criticism of Wagner as musical and cultural phenomenon, as well as in the substantial body of fictional literature inspired by the Wagnerian phenomenon (above all the literature of the self-styled "decadent"

---

[1] See letter of 15 July 1878 to Mathilde Maier, quoted in Newman, 1946, pp. 518–519.

movement of the fin-de-siècle). The background of this morbid pre-occupation with Wagnerian causes and effects, then, can be identified with one of the fin-de-siècle's explosion of self-consciously constructed cultural trends, "-isms," or illnesses: that commonly known as "Wagnerism."

The association of Wagner and "decadence" is likewise central to Nietzsche's critique. The vocabulary of cultural pathology is, of course, an essentially figurative one, often evoking the theme of general social and cultural "decay"—a theme which preoccupied Wagner as much as it did Nietzsche. Yet the preponderance of the language of disease in Nietzsche's late anti-Wagnerian polemics (as in much other contemporary and subsequent literature) is nonetheless striking, especially when contrasted with the opposing claims of redemption and healing propounded by orthodox Wagnerian ideology. The paradox calls for some comment. But first let us analyze briefly Nietzsche's highly influential deployment of the pathological metaphor.

"Wagner's art is sick," he continues, in *The Case of Wagner.* "The problems he presents on the stage—all of them . . . hysterical cases—the convulsive nature of the emotional states he depicts, his overexcited sensibility . . . and not least of all his choice of heroes and heroines—consider them as physiological types (a pathological gallery!)—all of this taken together represents a profile of sickness that permits no further doubt. *Wagner est une névrose* [Wagner is a neurosis]" (Nietzsche, 1888b, p. 166). Of course, as Nietzsche must have understood, the fascination of this Wagnerian "gallery" lies precisely in the nature of its psychological portraits, as painted in both words and music. If he was truly opposed to psychoanalysis on stage, then Nietzsche was certainly fighting a losing battle against the emergent Zeitgeist. On the other hand, Nietzsche demonstrates his keen awareness of that same Zeitgeist in evoking the lurking dangers of cultural "degeneration," a primary symptom of the unhealthy modern condition:

> Perhaps nothing is better known today, at least nothing has been better studied, than the Protean character of degeneration that here conceals itself in the chrysalis of art and artist. Our physicians and physiologists confront their most interesting case in Wagner. . . . Precisely because nothing is more modern than this total sickness, this lateness and overexcitement of the nervous mechanism [*Maschinerie*], Wagner is the *modern artist par excellence* the Cagliostro of modernity [Nietzsche, 1888b, p. 166].

A rhetorical strategy behind Nietzsche's deployment of the pathological metaphor is his application of the language of infectious disease or other areas of internal medicine to matters of mental health or, more generally, cultural "health" (always a suspicious category, as Nietzsche ought to have realized), as well as aesthetic issues of perception and judgment. On the effects of "Wagnerism," for example, he writes:

> One pays heavily for being one of Wagner's disciples. I observe those youths who have been exposed to his infection for a long time. The first, relatively innocent effect is the deterioration of taste. Wagner has the same effect as the habitual consumption of alcohol. He neutralizes and obstructs the stomach with phlegm. Specific effect: degeneration of the sense of rhythm. . . . Considerably more dangerous is the deterioration of concepts. [The symptoms here:] The disciple is beyond science . . . he poses as a philosopher. He writes for the *Bayreuther Blätter*, and solves all problems in the name of the father, the son, and the holy *Meister* [Nietzsche, 1888b, pp. 184–185; cf. Nietzsche, 1988a, pp. 122–123].

Certainly there is a healthy element to this kind of skepticism with regard to the more ludicrous manifestations of early Wagnerism. But, as in his reference above to the "decay of the sense of rhythm," Nietzsche is also concerned with the directly "physical" effects of Wagner. Earlier, in *Die fröhliche Wissenschaft* ("The Gay Science") of 1882, Nietzsche offers brief chapters (afterwards incorporated into the pamphlet, "Nietzsche contra Wagner") on "Where I admire" [Wagner] and "Where I offer objections." His rather backhanded admirations are immediately qualified:

> This does *not* mean that I consider his music *healthy*. . . . My objections to the music of Wagner are physiological objections: why should I dress them up in aesthetic formulas? After all, aesthetics is nothing but a kind of applied physiology. . . . [The fact is] that I no longer breathe easily when this music begins to affect me; that my foot soon resents it and rebels; my foot feels the need for rhythm, dance, march. . . . But does not my *stomach* protest too, my heart, my circulation? Are not my intestines saddened? Don't I suddenly become hoarse? To listen to Wagner I need *pastilles Gérandel* [i.e. cough drops: not an uncommon reaction, to judge by the behavior of most audiences]. . . . Wagner makes [one] sick [*Wagner macht krank*] [Nietzsche, 1889b, p. 664; cf. Nietzsche, 1889a, p. 132].

"Wagner makes you sick." In what sense did Nietzsche believe that Wagner is hazardous to your health? Apart from dire prognoses about the short- or long-term effects of Wagnerian singing on the human voice (see the following section), Wagner and his music may well have been concretely identified with periods of physical suffering in Nietzsche's memory: his unpleasant experience of the first Bayreuth festival, for example, had much to do with the heat, the commotion, and the violent migraine headaches precipitated by his chronic eye troubles and other accumulated physical indispositions, as examined by Ernest Newman (1946) in considerable detail (pp. 491–539).[2] The famous rhetorical tactic of pitting Bizet's *Carmen* against Wagner's operas at the beginning of *Der Fall Wagner* rests as much on climactic as on cultural dichotomies; switching from Wagner to Bizet sounds here like a piece of medical advice for those suffering from a tubercular condition: "With this work (*Carmen*) one takes leave of the damp north, of all the steam of the Wagnerian ideal." Merimée's plot—passionate yet rational and linear—has that which "goes with the torrid zone: the dryness, the *limpidezza* in the air. In every respect, the climate is changed" (Nietzsche, 1888b, p. 158). The Wagnerian climate, on the other hand, breeds disease: "How harmful for me is this Wagnerian orchestral tone! I call it *scirocco*. I break out into a disagreeable sweat. *My* good weather is gone" (Nietzsche, 1888b, p. 157).

Wagner's neo-Hegelian realm of obscure "idealism" and symbol is also that of cold, fog, and clouds: Wagner himself is "*related* to such bad weather, *German* weather! Wotan is their god, but Wotan is the *god* of bad weather" (p. 178). For Nietzsche, the only true "redemption" (at this point) is *physical* redemption, redemption from the rheumatic world of Wagnerian myth to the relaxation of a Mediterranean vacation.

WAGNERIAN PATHOLOGY BEFORE NIETZSCHE

It was not only the general theme of cultural "degeneration" that Nietzsche could read in the Zeitgeist, however, but even the metaphor

---

[2] But see also Nietzsche, 1889a, p. 143 ("Wie ich von Wagner loskam," from *Nietzsche contra Wagner*) for an expression of Nietzsche's re-interpretation of the episode: " . . . als ich allein weiter ging, zitterte ich; nicht lange darauf war ich krank, mehr als krank, nämlich *müde* . . ." (cf. Nietzsche, 1889b, p. 676: "As I proceeded alone I trembled; not long after that, I was sick, more than sick, namely *weary* . . . ").

of Wagnerian "pathology" itself, particularly as a symptom of these larger modern ills. It is not uncommon to encounter the metaphor in criticism of earlier romantic music considered to be excessively "reflective" and demanding, unusually complex, chromatic, or otherwise technically arcane, aurally rebarbative, and expressively abstruse. In the most prominent cases of such criticism—as elicited by Beethoven's late works and some of the music of Chopin and Schumann—the pathological symptoms ascribed to the music are very likely inspired by knowledge of the composers' own medical conditions: Beethoven's deafness, irritability, and general physical deterioration in the 1820s; Chopin's "fragile" constitution, his hothouse salon environment, and the tubercular condition of his last decade; and the still contested issue of Schumann's mental illness (see Ostwald, 1985).

The famous anti-Wagnerian, Eduard Hanslick, had included a chapter on the "Aesthetic Reception of Music vs. the Pathological" in his 1854 treatise *Vom Musikalisch-Schönen* (On the Beautiful in Music). While Hanslick's treatise on musical aesthetics actually predates his real critical falling out with Wagner, from the 1860s and the period of *Die Meistersinger*, his denunciation of the "pathological" listening on general aesthetic terms embodies, not surprisingly, some basic premises of later criticism of Wagner's "unhealthy" effects. These premises, in fact, align Hanslick's critique of pathological listening in *Vom Musikalisch-Schönen* with later criticism of Wagner (his own and others) in a way that also distinguishes "the Wagner case" significantly from the cases of Beethoven, Chopin, or Schumann. That is, Hanslick is not concerned with reading musical works as symptoms of their composer's pathologies (deafness, physical weakness, madness), but with the relationship between music and listener.

Indeed, Hanslick's fifth chapter on "The Aesthetic vs. Pathological Reception of Music," as the title indicates, is an indictment of listening habits rather than musical styles (an indictment that continues to inform the ethics of "classical music" listening today, although it is becoming increasingly subject to reevaluation). Hanslick draws a dichotomy—perhaps too sharp—between a positively evaluated *active*, aesthetic, or analytical engagement with musical works (typically presupposed by the style of Viennese classicism) and a passive, sensual, unreflective consumption of music which he compares to the consumption of food, alcohol, or "narcotic" substances. Of this second class of listeners he asserts: "Their relation to music is not objective [*anschauend*], but *pathological*: a continual twilight of feeling, effusion, a constant to-and-fro within a tonal void" ("ein stetes Dämmern, Fühlen, Schwärmen, ein Hangen und Bangen im klingenden Nichts"—Hanslick, 1854, p. 71). Such listeners, he rather sententiously opines, "would be better served by such modern inventions as chloroform [*Schwefeläther*]. Indeed, such sedative narcotics [*Aethernarkose*] lull us into the most pleasant waking dreams, our whole organism is infused by a gentle intoxication, yet without having to resort to vulgar tippling—which itself is not without musical effects, however" (p. 72). The blame for this manner of reception (or consumption) of music attaches to both the music and the listener; the merely "physical effects of music are exerted in proportion to the sickly irascibility [*krankhaften Gereiztheit*] of the nervous system encountering the music" (p. 74).

At the same time Hanslick was articulating this critique of "pathological" listening, Wagner's first important works were just beginning to be taken up by enterprising theaters throughout Europe, and his overheated aesthetic polemics (such as *Opera and Drama*) were making a stir in critical circles. The frenzied bacchanalia of the *Tannhäuser* Overture and the visionary-mystical *Schwärmerei* of the *Lohengrin* Prelude, in their different ways, seemed to be a dangerously new kind of music that was calculated to act on the senses and "nerves" of its listeners while completely bypassing their minds. Such music withheld the customary outlines of classical phraseology and formal design, so it seemed, while it dazzled and seduced the senses by means of unusual chords and progressions, sinuous melodic chromaticism, and brilliant orchestral effects (shrill woodwinds, turbulent string figurations, and garish percussive touches in the Venusberg music, for example, or ethereal string harmonics and a kaleidoscopic, mesmerizingly gradual unfolding of instrumental timbres in the *Lohengrin* Prelude). Wagner's music was increasingly accused of lacking "resting points," clear cadential articulations necessary (it was felt) for the kind of active, engaged listening advocated by Hanslick. With this music, it seemed, the audience could do little more than passively submit to the orchestral and vocal torrent that besieged them.

Such responses were widely shared, while they might be variously evaluated according to the cultural or even political disposition of the listener (Wagner's revolutionary sympathies were universally known, and very often read into the character of his music). Louis Ehlert (1859), a critic who first encountered the music of Tannhäuser in the 1850s, was at first "repulsed" by it, and yet quickly succumbed to its fascinations, resigning himself to the "narcotic" potency of this new kind of music:

> I cannot describe to you the active displeasure this piece [the *Tann-häuser* Overture] aroused in me on first hearing, what a repulsive, whining effect the motif of the Venusberg had on my ganglia [*welch ein abscheuliches, auf mein Gangliensystem wirkendes Gewinsel mir das Motiv des Venusbergs schien*], how dreadfully poor and flat Tannhäuser's song in B major [sic] seemed to me. . . . Even today I am far from considering the *Tannhäuser* Overture as an art-work on the level of [Beethoven's] *Coriolan* Overture, but I have gradually accustomed myself to it, and played before the curtain, it transports me into a narcotic state [*in einem narkotischen Zustand*] of the most pleasing kind [p. 159].

It seems to have been *Tannhäuser*, among the earlier operas, that routinely inspired such moral condemnation and warnings about the possible ill effects of its music on the psyche. A reviewer of the early Wiesbaden production of *Tannhäuser* in 1852 (thus before Hanslick had diagnosed the general symptoms of "pathological" listening) described the effect of its larger ensemble scenes as "a fight to the death" between orchestral and vocal forces, in which "the voices are bound to be the losers, while the effect on listeners must surely be to upset their nerves (*die Zuhörer aber nervenkrank werden*) (Anonymous, 1852, p. 141). As in many such early responses to this music, however, the blame is not cast on Wagner as an aesthetically corrupt individual; rather, the music is read as a symptom of a broader modern cultural malaise. A certain Mme. Marie Gjertz, discoursing on music "from the moral and religious point of view" in 1859 (the date of Wagner's *Tristan*) compares the effects of "modern music" in general with the insalubrious vapors of a "decomposing corpse": the psychic emanations of such music are "no less harmful to the health of the spirit—make no mistake!—than pestilential air to the health of the body" (Gjertz, 1859, p. 153).

As with physical narcotic substances, the effects of the Wagnerian musical narcotic were evaluated very differently according to different perspectives. Where some warned about deleterious long-term effects on the aesthetic body politic (so to speak), many reckless individuals were nonetheless succumbing to addiction. Baudelaire (1861) famously reveled in the intoxicating effects of Wagner's music, especially the *Lohengrin* Prelude and *Tannhäuser* Overture (with the new Venusberg music), which he heard while Wagner was attempting an international breakthrough with *Tannhäuser* in Paris: "It sometimes seems, in listening to this ardent and despotic music, that one finds depicted the vertiginous images of an opium dream, set against the dark depths, torn by reverie" (p. 208). Listening to the *Tannhäuser* Overture, "the nerves thrill in unison with the melody, from the very first measures; all flesh that remembers will begin to tremble" (p. 222). In the music of the Venusberg (*"la partie voluptueuse de l'ouverture"*) we "breath a perfumed yet oppressive atmosphere, illuminated by a rosy glow that emanates not from the sun; we are like Tannhäuser himself who, saturated with enervating delights, wishes for sorrow!" (p. 223).

Baudelaire and the Paris of this epoch (around 1860) have often been identified with the emergence of a distinctive (if elusive) aesthetic of "modernism." The isolation of this historical moment may seem somewhat arbitrary, but there is much evidence to suggest that a consciousness of a new, provocative, destabilizing culture was indeed becoming widespread just about this time—part of that Zeitgeist tapped by Nietzsche in his later attacks on Wagnerism and modern "degeneration." Wagner's so-called "music of the future" (a catchword of the 1860s) and its purportedly "intoxicating," formally and harmonically anarchistic traits were clearly at the center of this perception. An anonymous editorial on "The Representatives of Modern Musical Directions" published in the Berlin music journal *Echo* in 1861 traces themes of cultural "sickness" and degeneration back to Schumann's music, and forward to the present baleful influence of Wagner: "Wagner's manner of feeling [*Empfindungsweise*] is so unhealthy, at its core, so lacking in human beauty, that its influence on our atmosphere—already burdened with so many noxious fumes—will hardly be a salutary one" (Anonymous, 1861, p. 346). One year later the pianist and composer Louis Köhler (1862) found it timely to publish an essay, "On the True Purpose and Value of Music, with Respect to Narcotic Composers" (*Neue Berliner Musik-Zeitung*, 1862). (Köhler, in fact, was a vocal advocate of Wagner's and Liszt's *Zukunftsmusik*: his notion of "narcotic" music appears not to have referred to the inebriating, emotionally unsettling effects of "modern" music, but to innocuous styles of salon music—berceuses, barcarolles, and "songs without words"—that lulled the listener into a soporific inattention.)

It is perhaps not surprising, then (despite Köhler's polemical inversion of the "narcotic" trope), to find an amateur musical health-specialist, editorializing in an anonymous "op-ed" piece in the resurrected *Allegmeine musikalische Zeitung* ("E.R.," 1866), already identifying the antidote to this degenerative addiction to Wagner and to effect-laden operatic music in general in "absolute music"—an antidote provided in potent form, he claims, in the music of the young Johannes Brahms. For all his critical abuse of Meyerbeer, Wagner (so this writer asserts) has only exacerbated the sensual-musical excesses of French grand opera, intensifying the "demonic glow of colors, the numbing dynamic levels (*betäubenden materiellem Getöse*), the effects and stimuli of all kinds" pioneered by Meyerbeer. What *is* surprising, on the other hand, is how this critic identifies Wagner's relentless exaltation of his masculine heroes and the concomitant "unconditional subjugation' of the self-sacrificing women as one dramatic source of his unhealthy effect on the public mind and mores: "this fundamental idea is driven to such extremes that . . . one is forced to conclude that, rather than a beneficial influence with regard to truth and naturalness of feeling, or with regard to health and harmony among the people (*nach Seite der Gesundheit und Harmonie des Volks*), it can only encourage a romantic overexcitement, as a sickness (eine romanhafte *Überspannung* . . . , *als Krankheit*)" ("E.R.," 1866, p. 64). "Real music lovers," he submits, will seek a more healthy alternative to all of this in the concert hall, "the last refuge of pure music."

With the premiere of *Tristan und Isolde* several years later the concept of musical "intoxication" discovered a whole new paradigm, which would take the better part of a generation to absorb. No end of early critics decried this as a "music for the nerves," a dangerous stimulant for overly excitable modern constitutions (especially feminine ones). Others reacted primarily to the "narcotic length" of Wagner's new music dramas.[3] The "dangers" of Tristan become alarmingly real when Wagner's first Tristan, the powerful tenor Ludwig Schnorr von Carolsfeld, collapsed within a month of the premiere. It was hard to resist interpreting the circumstantial evidence that the exertions of the role had proven to be his downfall; even Wagner was inclined to believe so,

---

[3] For example, one of the notices on the 1865 Munich premiere complained that the overlong spinning out of the opening scene of Act II (Isolde's dialogue with Brangäne in anticipation of her upcoming tryst) had a "narcotically numbing effect" on the listener (Anonymous, 1865, p. 189).

as Zuckermann (1964) demonstrates, though he refrained from admitting it publicly (p. 58). And quite apart from the physical demands on the performers, Wagner was acutely aware of the cognitive and psychological demands he was placing on his audience—and their "nervous systems"—with this radical work. "My child!" he confided to the muse of this passionate work, Mathilde Wesendonck, in a letter dating from mid-April 1859, "this Tristan is turning into something *terrible!* This final Act!!! I fear the opera will be banned . . . only mediocre performances can save me! Perfectly *good* ones will be bound to drive people mad" (cited from Spencer and Millington, 1988, p. 452). While Wagner's newest music quickly began to thrill a small, receptive element of the public, there remained a large portion who mistrusted its "effects," and worried about what such things portended for the future health of the musical culture. "What the 'good musicians' (a synonym for musical conservatives) objected to in Wagner was that the idea of the *Gesamt-kunstwerk* smacked of amateurishness," writes Carl Dahlhaus (1992):

> [They suspected] that a leitmotif technique which replaced musical coherence with the suggestive effect of repetitions was a kind of music for the unmusical; or that the intoxication bought about by the music drama was based on a profoundly destructive penchant for the amorphous and the anarchical. In the final analysis this comes to one and the same thing: that in the case of Wagner the music as such, independent of the theatrical effect (which in the 19th century, despite Schiller, was still mistrusted on moral grounds), was questionable in some admittedly elusive way [p. 312].

WAGNER AND *DÉCADENCE*

Sickness—corporeal as well as psychological—is a predominant theme in the literature of the turn-of-the-century "decadent" movement: and an age preoccupied with "the abnormal cultivation of the self, a guilt-ridden sexuality and . . . the expression of psychic disturbance," in the words of Raymond Furness (1982), would naturally turn to Wagner for inspiration (p. 14).[4]

---

[4] See also T. W. Adorno (1952):

The socially determined experience of pleasure as unfreedom transforms libido into sickness, and so we see how, with the cry of 'too much!', Tannhäuser becomes conscious of his own enjoyment as a weakness. . . . The experience of pleasure as sickness permeates Wagner's entire oeuvre. . . . Sickness and desire become con-

This inspiration was drawn above all from certain suggestive dramatic motifs in the operas: the dynamics of eroticism and religion in *Tannhäuser* and *Parsifal*; intoxicating self-abandon and oblivion in *Tristan und Isolde*; the incest theme in *Die Walküre*; and the larger theme of familial, dynastic, or racial decline inscribed in *Götterdämmerung*. (Adorno draws particular attention to the associations of sexuality, guilt, and disease in Wagner: cf. n. 4.)

But then as now, the allure of Wagner's psychological symbolism was reinforced by the experience of the music. Even the musically untrained were in some degree sensitive to the expressive implications of Wagnerian techniques (especially in the works from *Tristan* on): the "decay" of traditional tonality and phraseology effected by his lushly scored chromaticisms and the sinuous waves of his "endless melody," alternately languid and passionate. Surely *this* was the music of decadence?

Something of these effects seems to have been projected into the very features of the composer himself, to judge by Renoir's late Wagner portrait: Peter Conrad has described it as a "face decomposed and drained of color, the eyes rheumy and lips pursed in sickly connoisseurship of sensation; the head is surrounded by an impressionistic blizzard of streaks and daubs, threatening a dissolution of form. . . . It is not Wotan's head, but Alberich's, feverish, obsessive, expiring" (cited from Furness, 1982, p. 31).

There are two sides to the "pathological metaphor" as it relates to the Decadent movement. On one hand, there are the critics of the movement, such as Max Nordau (1892), whose once-influential tome on the subject of cultural "degeneration" lamented the imminent decay of European moral and aesthetic values, and identified Wagner as a primary agent behind this cultural "sickness"[5] (see also Beckett, 1979; Furness, 1982). (Ironically, Nordau applies to Wagner the very term—*"Entartung"* or degeneracy—with which the Nazis would later

---

founded in a point of view that imagines that the forces of life can only be maintained by the suppression of life. . . . In a regression familiar from the process of bourgeois education and known to psychoanalysis as 'syphilophobia,' sex and sexual disease become identical [p. 93].
See also Furness (1982, chapter 2), for a detailed summary of Wagnerian themes in the literature of decadence from Baudelaire through Huysmans, D'Annuzio, and Mann.

[5] Note the specifically clinical terminology of Nordau's chapter headings: "The Symptoms," "Diagnosis," and "Etiology" in the opening section, and "Prognosis" and "Therapeutics" as concluding rubrics. See also Book II, chapter 5 on "The Richard Wagner Cult."

stigmatize *their* notion of "sick" art, to which Wagner had become the healthy, pure Aryan antipode). Nietzsche may be seen as the original spokesperson of this critique, yet his own relationship to "decadence" (as to Wagner) is notoriously ambivalent, and is much more a matter of guilt-laden self-identification than sententious moralizing. (Note that Nietzsche also spoke of emergent German nationalism as a "cultural sickness" and as the German "national neurosis," for example in *Ecce Homo*.)

On the other hand, among the "decadents" themselves, beginning with Baudelaire, the themes of decay, "sickness," self-obsession, and self-indulgence are all reconstructed as *positive* values: conditions favorable to psychological insight and artistic creativity (Koppen, 1992). And it was from this perspective, of course, that they embraced Wagner as one of their own. Given this reversal of values, it is not surprising to find the "decadent" Wagnerians eulogizing the music in much the same terms as its detractors used to condemn it. Following the lead of Baudelaire (in his 1861 essay on the Paris *Tannhäuser* overture), both parties identified narcotic and aphrodisiac qualities in Wagner's music—an opiate to lull the intellect and heighten the senses. For one party this spelled release, abandonment, inspiration, even a "redemption" of sorts from prosaic reality; for the other party, it spelled the deterioration of taste and the senses, weakness and passivity of the aesthetic faculties, and general perdition. In either case, Wagnerian "sickness" was seen as the symbolic condition of the modern artist.

WAGNERIAN "PATHOLOGY" IN THE WORKS OF MANN

This idea we find corroborated in the early works of Thomas Mann. As a conscious heir to the tradition of literary "decadence," while at the same time keenly aware of Nietzsche's critique, Mann was particularly sensitive to the "pathology" of Wagner. In *Buddenbrooks* the last scion of a declining merchant family, young Hanno Buddenbrook displays all the signs of a decadent Wagnerian from his earliest years: constitutional weakness, morbid hypersensitivity and introversion, a disinclination toward practical matters, and (later on) a penchant for keyboard improvisation in the manner of *Tristan*. Immediately following one such Tristanesque improvisation Hanno succumbs to the typhoid fever which brings about his early death. In Mann's novella *Tristan* (1902), the pale and fragile Gabriele Klöterjahn is sent to an Alpine sanatorium for the treatment of an initially vague respiratory ailment. Left alone in the salon one afternoon with her slightly ludicrous decadent-aesthete admirer, Detlev Spinell, Gabriele breaks her doctors' injunction against musical performance and succumbs to the piano score of *Tristan und Isolde* lying in temptation's way. Within days, the terminal stages of tuberculosis have set in. In *The Blood of the Wälsungs* (1905), a pair of idle and over-refined twins from a nouveau-riche Jewish family in a fashionable Berlin suburb act out an incestuous Wagnerian parody in the context of a performance of *Die Walküre*. Among the verbal leitmotifs applied here by Mann is a recurrent description of the twins in the classic terminology of Wagnerian decadence: their "languid yet voluptuous abandon" and their behavior, "like self-centered invalids who absorb themselves in trifles, as narcotics to console themselves for the loss of hope." (Both the "Love-death" idea from *Tristan* and the incest motif of *Die Walküre* had already figured in a number of fictional works from this period; see Furness, 1982, Chapter 2.)

Did Mann believe that overexposure to Wagner could lead to typhus or tubercular infection, or perhaps hasten their progress, or that it promoted spiritual enervation and moral degeneracy? Certainly he inherited Nietzsche's profound ambivalence on the subject of Wagner. Like Nietzsche, he felt the need as a young intellectual to escape the overbearing presence of Wagner's mind and art. "As a thinker and personality he seemed to me suspect," wrote Mann in an essay of 1911, "as an artist irresistible, if also deeply questionable in terms of the nobility, purity, and wholesomeness of his influence" (p. 46). In this same essay Mann appears, significantly, as an early exponent of the "new classicism," the modernist aesthetic of the early twentieth century which set out to exorcise the debilitating, narcotic opulence of decadent Romanticism in the name of a healthy simplicity and objectivity. The general association of Classicism with "health" and Romanticism with "sickness" can be traced back to Goethe, in fact, and the figures of Goethe and Wagner represent a similar dichotomy in the aesthetic thought of both Nietzsche and Mann. (Schiller, incidentally, had voiced his suspicions regarding music's inherent privileging of "sensations" over ideas in his 1793 essay, "On the Pathetic," where he noted that musical listeners are easily prey to "symptoms of intoxication.")

It is true that the deaths of Hanno Buddenbrook and Gabriele Klöterjahn can, by narrative inference, be related partly to stress induced by their direct physical (as well as emotional) engagement with the performance of Wagnerian music. In both cases they "overdose" on this perniciously seductive musical narcotic. It would probably be more apt, however, to diagnose Wagner as a *symptom* rather than a cause in these cases. Hanno Buddenbrook is characterized from the beginning as lacking a "will to live"; he seeks in Wagner (or in music in general) a means of escape. Gabriele Klöterjahn is similarly marked from the outset as a consumptive case, a generally frail and potentially sensitive figure, but not initially as a "Wagnerian." Neither is Wagner *directly* responsible for the less severe cases of Detlev Spinell and Siegmund Aarenhold—their creative impotence and general lack of purpose. In both cases Wagner merely represents an overwhelming aesthetic force whose very potency only serves to highlight their own existing condition.

In all these contexts, Mann's fundamental admiration for Wagner as an artist plainly shows through. He always saw in Wagner a persuasive dramatist, an acute psychologist, and above all a consummate musical craftsman. Mann could read Nietzsche's vehement critique as "a panegyric in reverse, another form of eulogy . . . , an expression of love-hate, an act of self-mortification" (Mann, 1911, pp. 100–101). And while Nietzsche objected to Wagner as cultural "Calgiostro" and charlatan, posing as a modern savior, he continued to admire the quality of the music itself. Mann, after all, found in the structural detail of the music drama (and its leitmotifs) inspiration for his own narrative technique.

Still, Wagner's work appealed to an element in Mann's own psychology which he evidently felt the need to resist: the aggressively domineering quality of Wagner's mythical–symbolic rhetoric; the seductive and hypnotic wiles of his harmonic language, of his instrumentation, of his subtly evolving motivic web—all of these things tended to induce a passive surrender of the aesthetic consciousness which seems to have been central to the "decadent" experience of Wagner and to have prompted the health-warnings posted by Nietzsche and Mann (and others besides—Eduard Hanslick, for example).[6]

---

[6] Cf. Hanslick on "pathological listening" in *Vom Musikalisch-Schönen* (chapter 5, "The Aesthetic Perception of Music vs. the Pathological," discussed above) and the reference to Hanslick in Beckett (1981): "That the musical tradition should become contaminated by specific content of such a questionable kind [*Parsifal*, e.g.] was, in Hanslick's view, a menace to be resisted" (p. 105). Beckett also cites Hanslick's review of the 1882 premiere: "We can almost sense a decaying mentality when a modern artist sees in the relic of the Grail and in sacred miracles the mission of German art, and proposes herewith to effect the regeneration of humanity" (p. 106). Also see the reference to Hanslick in Ridley (1987, p. 54): "Hanslick, who had written of the dangers of the 'unhealthy stimulation' of Wagner's music. . . . "

SICKNESS OR REDEMPTION?

If Wagner is not, after all, a disease per se, what about the contrary claim—the power of the *Gesamtkunstwerk* to cleanse, heal, and renew the individual as well as the collective social psyche? Did this signify nothing more than a cultural analogue to some nineteenth-century quack panacea—a musical "tonic" without any practical effect (at best), or one that would, according to its detractors, literally "wash the brain" of all that was still healthy and rational? For Nietzsche, there was no paradox, since "the *need* for salvation . . . is the sincerest expression of *décadence*" (Nietzsche, 1888b, p. 191). "He flatters every nihilistic (Buddhistic) instinct and disguises it in music; he flatters everything Christian, every religious expression of decadence" (p. 183). Others, like Wagner's pragmatic English biographer, Ernest Newman (1924), have simply dismissed the theme of redemption as obsolete, essentially meaningless outside the mythic storyland of the music drama. Or, as Adorno (1952) puts it, "Wagnerian redemption . . . is the ultimate phantasmagoria" (p. 149)—i.e., a musico-theatrical illusion conjured up from "mere subjectivity," without substance.[7] One might also recall here the criticism that has been leveled at the seemingly "artificial"—though effective—reprise and apotheosis of the so-called "Redemption-motif" at the close of *Götterdämmerung* (see Vaget, 1987, pp. 91ff.).

At any rate, if we agree with Erwin Koppen (1992) that Wagnerism denotes a phenomenon which has long since become "purely historical" (pp. 343–344), then the same can probably be said of the ideology of Wagnerian "redemption" on the larger, sociocultural level. But what about the individual's experience of Wagner? Is Wagner still a threat to our well-being and mental equilibrium, if he ever really was; or is he (still) a source of healing psychic therapy (if he ever really was that, either)? I would hope that it would not be too naive to say that the "threat" sensed by Nietzsche and Mann seems largely faded into history, while the therapeutic and cathartic value of his works remains potent. Perhaps such a therapeutic and cathartic value can be attributed in

---

[7] "For true transcendence it substitutes the mirage of the enduring, upwards-soaring individual who vanishes into thin air at the moment of his annihilation. . . . In the innermost core of Wagner's idea of redemption dwells nothingness. It too is empty. Wagner's phantasmagoria is a mirage because it is the manifestation of the null and void. And this defines the impulse underlying Wagner's style. . . . " (Adorno, 1952, p. 149). One sometimes wonders why Adorno felt it was worth writing a book on Wagner at all.

some sense to the very tensions this earlier generation sensed in the Wagnerian oeuvre: Wagner's "healthy brand of sickness, his diseased brand of heroism," as Mann (1933) wrote, "are just one instance of the contradictions and convolutions inherent in his nature, its ambiguity and equivocality" (p. 128).[8] Like the concept of "Romanticism" itself, Mann adds, Wagner's character remains so "complex and elusive" that one is finally forced to abandon any hope of a single, satisfactory definition. Like any complex psychological phenomenon, Wagner and his works encompass a multitude of polarities, which remain in many ways the essence of his enduring fascination.

REFERENCES

Adorno, T. W. (1952), *In Search of Wagner* (orig. *Versuch über Wagner*, 1952), tr. R. Livingstone. Manchester: NLB.

Anonymous review (1852), *Tannhäuser* in Wiesbaden. In: *Süddeutsche Musikzeitung*, vol. 1.

Anonymous editorial (1865), Die Repräsentanten der modernen Musikrichtungen (signed "Rec."), *Berliner Musik-Zeitung Echo* 11 (1861).

Anonymous review (1865), Die Aufführung von Richard Wagner's *Tristan und Isolde* in München. In: *Blätter für Theater, Musik, und Kunst* 11.

Baudelaire, C. (1861), Richard Wagner et *Tannhäuser* à Paris. In: *Oeuvres complètes (L'Art Romantique)*, ed. M. J. Crépet. Paris: Louis Conrad, 1925, pp. 199–252.

Beckett, L. (1979), Wagner and his critics. In: *The Wagner Companion*, ed. P. Burbidge & R. Sutton. New York: Cambridge University Press, pp. 365–388.

—— (1981), *Richard Wagner: Parsifal.* Cambridge, U.K.: Cambridge University Press.

Dahlhaus, C. (1992), The music (The charge of dilettantism: Wagner and modernism). In: *Wagner Handbook*, ed. U. Müller & P. Wapnewski, tr. & ed. J. Deathridge. Cambridge, MA: Harvard University Press, pp. 311–314.

Ehlert, L. (1859), *Briefe über die Musik an eine Freundin* (1st ed. 1859). 3rd ed. Berlin: Behr's Buchhandlung, 1879.

"E. R." (1866), Die moderne "grosse" Oper und die Musik im Concert. Meyerbeer, Wagner und—Brahms. In: *Allgemeine musikalische Zeitung*, vol. 1, pp. 62–65.

Furness, R. (1982), *Wagner and Literature.* New York: St. Martin's Press.

---

[8] See also Nietzsche's comments about the benefits of his "recovery" from Wagner—as a positive experience in itself—in the Epilogue to "Nietzsche contra Wagner" (Nietzsche, 1889b, p. 680).

Gjertz, M. (1859), La musique au point de vue moral et religieux. Orig. in: *Revue et gazette musicale,* 21 August 1859. Rpt. in: *Neue Wiener Musik-Zeitung* vol. 8 (1859).

Hanslick, E. (1854), *Vom Musikalisch-Schönen* (orig. ed. 1854). Darmstadt: Wissenschaftliche Buchgesellschaft, 1981.

Koppen, E. (1992), Wagnerism as concept and phenomenon. In: *Wagner Handbook,* ed. U. Müller & P. Wapnewski, tr. & ed. J. Deathridge. Cambridge MA: Harvard University Press, pp. 343–353.

Kossmaly, C. (1862), Über den wahren Zweck und Werth der Musik mit Bezug auf narkotischen Komponisten. In: *Neue Berliner Musik-Zeitung,* 16.

Mann, T. (1902), *Tristan.* In: *Stories of Three Decades,* tr. H. T. Lowe-Porter. New York: Knopf, 1936, pp. 133–166.

——— (1905), *Blood of the Wälsungs.* In: *Stories of Three Decades,* tr. H. T. Lowe-Porter. New York: Knopf, 1936, pp. 297–319.

——— (1911), Coming to terms with Richard Wagner. In: *Thomas Mann: Pro and Contra Wagner* [selected writings], tr. A. Blunden. Chicago: University of Chicago Press, 1985, pp. 45–47.

——— (1933), Sorrows and grandeur of Richard Wagner. In: *Thomas Mann: Pro and Contra Wagner,* tr. A. Blunden. Chicago: University of Chicago Press, 1985, pp. 91–148.

Newman, E. (1924), *Wagner as Man and Artist.* New York: Knopf.

——— (1946). *Life of Richard Wagner,* Vol. 4 (1866–1883). New York: Knopf.

Nietzsche, F. (1888a), *Der Fall Wagner.* In: *Der Fall Wagner: Schriften und Aufzeichnungen über Richard Wagner,* ed. with an afterword, D. Borchmeyer. Frankfurt a.M.: Insel, 1983, pp. 93–129.

——— (1888b), *The Case of Wagner.* In: *The Birth of Tragedy and the Case of Wagner,* tr. Walter Kaufmann. New York: Vintage.

——— (1889a), Nietzsche contra Wagner. In: *Der Fall Wagner: Schriften und Aufzeichnungen über Richard Wagner,* ed. with an afterword, D. Borchmeyer. Frankfurt a.M.: Insel, pp. 130–152.

——— (1889b), Nietzsche contra Wagner. In: *The Portable Nietzsche,* tr. & ed. W. Kaufmann. Harmondsworth, U.K., Penguin Books, pp. 661–683.

Nordau, M. (1892), *Degeneration* (orig. *Entartung,* Berlin, 1892). New York: D. Appleton, 1895.

Ostwald, P. (1985), *Robert Schumann: The Inner Voices of a Musical Genius.* Boston, MA: Northeastern University Press.

Ridley, H. (1987), *Thomas Mann: Buddenbrooks.* Cambridge, U.K.: Cambridge University Press.

Schiller, F. (1793). *Über das Pathetische.*

Spencer, S., & Millington, B., Trans. & Eds. (1988), *Selected Letters of Richard Wagner.* New York: W. W. Norton.

Vaget, H. (1987), Strategies for redemption: *Der Ring des Nibelungen* and *Faust.* In: *Wagner in Retrospect,* ed. L. R. Shaw, N. R. Cirillo, & M. S. Miller. Amsterdam: Rodopi, pp. 91–105.

Zuckerman, E. (1964), *The First Hundred Years of Wagner's "Tristan."* New York: Columbia University Press.

11

Panel Discussion on Performance, Interpretation, Staging, and Audience Response to the *Ring*

Moderator: David Littlejohn, writer; critic; Professor of Journalism at the University of California, Berkeley.

PANELISTS

Laurie Feldman, stage director *Das Rheingold* and *Götterdämmerung* in 1990 San Francisco Opera *Ring* cycles.

Herta Glaz, mezzo soprano; Adjunct Professor of Voice, University of California, Los Angeles; formerly sang with Metropolitan, San Francisco and other companies.

Hans Hotter, bass baritone, teacher and noted interpreter of Wotan and other roles at the Bayreuth Festspielhaus, Metropolitan Opera, San Francisco Opera, and many other international companies.

Janis Martin, soprano, performed two of the Brünnhildes in 1990 San Francisco *Ring* cycles.

Franz Mazura, bass, performed Alberich in 1990 San Francisco Opera *Ring* cycles.

Donald Runnicles, conductor of two San Francisco Opera 1990 *Ring* cycles.

Steven Sokolow, M.A., President, Wagner Society of Northern California.

Littlejohn: It's really quite extraordinary. If you want to talk about experiencing a genuine live *Ring* production on a slightly grander scale than the one we just saw at the Opera House, you could hardly come up with a more impressive list than ours today which includes a conductor; two directors; a Wotan; an Alberich who has also played Gunther; a

Brünnhilde who has also sung Sieglinde, and a Waltraute, Fricka, and Norn. And among the people on this afternoon's panel—plus, speaking for all of us, the President of the Northern California Wagner Society.

Let me just mention something about each of them before we begin. Herta Glaz sang at San Francisco Opera between 1939 and 1951, at the Metropolitan Opera as well, and has played the roles of Fricka, Waltraute, a Norn, and one of the Rhinemaidens.

It seems to me an extraordinary honor to have among us a man who I think is the greatest Wotan of the last 50 years, Hans Hotter, who according to my records, began making recordings of Wotan's selections from Act III of *Die Walküre* in 1934, Act II in 1938, and is strongly identified as a pioneer with the Wagner grandsons in the new Bayreuth productions where he performed from 1953 to 1958, and then again in 1966, as well as singing Wotan at Covent Garden a number of times, at the Metropolitan, at Paris, at La Scala, at Vienna. He is featured on four recordings, including the celebrated Knappertsbusch and Solti recordings of the *Ring* in the role of Wotan, and he himself produced the *Ring* at Covent Garden in 1964 and '65 with Georg Solti conducting, and Günther Schneider-Siemssen designing.

Steven Sokolow is President of the Wagner Society of Northern California and is letting me steal the biographies for the remaining members of the panel, all participants in this season's *Ring* in San Francisco.

Donald Runnicles, making his San Francisco and his *Ring* conducting debut, is General Music Director of the Freiburg Opera, who spent seven years at Mannheim where he conducted over 40 operas. He has been principal conductor at Hanover and began a long association in 1987 with the Hamburg Staatsoper. He also spent several seasons at Bayreuth assisting James Levine, Peter Schneider, and Georg Solti in the *Ring*, as well as assisting Levine at the Metropolitan where Runnicles made his debut two years ago, conducting the three-act version of Aban Berg's *Lulu*.

Laurie Feldman, who is serving this year as the Stage Director of *Das Rheingold* and *Götterdämmerung*, has been associated with the Opera for the last nine years. A native San Franciscan, she has been Assistant Stage

Manager for more than 25 productions, Assistant Director for more than 20, assisting such directors as Lotfi Mansouri, Michael Hampe, John Copley, and Nikolaus Lehnhoff, the producer of our *Ring*, on his production of *Salome*. She has also worked at Santa Fe Opera and Canadian Opera and has directed her own productions of operas at the Carmel Bach Festival and Marin Opera.

Our Alberich, perhaps the best known Alberich of this generation, is Franz Mazura. He has performed this role and that of Gunther at Bayreuth and in many other venues. He made his American debut here in San Francisco in 1968 as Jokanaan in *Salome* and his roles at the Metropolitan have included Gurnemanz, Klingsor, Alberich, and Dr. Schön in *Lulu* which he sang in the first complete three-act performance at the Paris Opera.

Janis Martin, California's own Brünnhilde, whom we've also heard as Sieglinde, is a graduate of San Francisco's Merola Opera Program who made her debut here in 1960 and has since performed some 25 roles. She has also sung Brangäne (actually we have two Brangänes at the table because that was another of Herta Glaz's roles in San Francisco a few years earlier), Sieglinde in *Die Walküre*, Kundry, and most recently she is being heard this season here as Brünnhilde.

Well, with a cast like this and the little time we have, there are almost too many questions that could be thrown at them. Let me just begin with a couple of questions that I raised in the articles I wrote for the program book this season on productions of the *Ring*.

I looked at reviews, descriptions, memoirs, photographs, articles written about some 103 productions of the complete *Ring* since 1876, most notably the 30 complete *Ring*s that have been staged in the last 20 years. An extraordinary flowering of sometimes perverse, sometimes maddening, sometimes magnificent *Ring*s. The two questions that critics most often raise in trying to judge the rightness or wrongness of any approach, musical, scenic, or dramatic, to a production of Wagner's *Ring of the Nibelung* seem to be these: (1) Is this what Wagner wanted, and (2) are you doing what the music tells you to do? Both of these struck me as being somewhat problematic and not at all clearcut questions. (A) Why should we care what Wagner wanted? and (B) is it all that clear what the music is telling us to do? So anyone who would like to leap into either of those questions can go right ahead.

Janis Martin: It's not possible to answer those questions in twenty-five words or less, but I don't think we can take Wagner so literally today because he would have done it differently now than he would have many years ago. He was a very, very modern and progressive person. And I think as far as knowing what the music has to say, that's very obvious. I don't think there's a question of a doubt what the music has to say. Hans, what do you have to say about that?

Hans Hotter: I dislike the idea that Wagner would have composed it differently today.

Janis Martin: No, composed it differently, no. He would have staged it differently maybe because the theatre now just has more possibilities.

Hans Hotter: Doesn't it go with the composition?

Janis Martin: Well, I mean, he would have had different possibilities now.

Hans Hotter: So I do not like the idea because of what he could have written musically. And I don't like to imagine Wagner's *Tristan* or something else as of 1990. I prefer the one of 1865. Therefore, I think this is not a good enough reason for me to say he would have written it differently today.

Janis Martin: But you can't do it the same every time, that's the thing.

Hans Hotter: That's a different story. The question is what do you want. What I personally dislike is the idea that we should always be criticized or looked upon as being old-fashioned just because we have certain respect and admiration for an artist's basic ideas. And as long as the music is not deformed, I'm quite happy to see another production. But not if the music is just sort of pushed back on the side, is not regarded.

Janis Martin: I agree with you one hundred percent.

Herta Glaz: I agree also with you. But my question is whether a very contemporary—what we might call contemporary version, like the one we saw here with a business-suited man on stage—does that bring the operas actually closer to the audience today than doing them the way Wagner wanted? Why would we not find that the audience has enough imagination to transform what Wagner wanted into our modern time.

Hans Hotter: I think it's mostly a cheap excuse to keep saying that we need something new. I think the audience wants the music in the first place and I think it is important that you stick to this point.

Then . . . (to Mazura) . . . you want to say something?

Franz Mazura: It's a combined thing with Wagner between music and production. What I found with the most modern productions is that they take away the imagination from the audience. They give them the imagination from the producer in so strong a way that you lose your own imagination. And there's something else. There's too much acting going on on stage. It's overpowering you and the sense overpowers you so you don't hear the music any more.

Hans Hotter: I feel that you must be able to improve the quality of performance in every respect. The audience would be much happier even if they were faced with a production they cannot understand if the quality of the opera performance were so great that it would free them from having to think about anything else.

Franz Mazura: I like most productions if they don't do it like the last one I was in. It was the kind where you have to make some action on stage for every accent in the music. Too much. That way the high points of acting are gone. But you have to do modern things and bring things from these modern insights into normal old-fashioned productions.

Hans Hotter: Yes, I think you should allow that.

David Littlejohn: Could I ask Laurie Feldman, since you are, at least nominally, responsible for what we're seeing on stage in *Das Rheingold* and *Götterdämmerung* this year, do you have any problems with Loge in the nineteenth century costume, or the modern-dress Gibichungs, or the sort of copy of a Caspar David Friedrich painting we see in the opening of the *Ring*—that kind of thing. Do these trouble you in any sense?

Laurie Feldman: Can I say something first in defense of producers? If we're asking the question, are we doing what the music is telling us, one of the things to remember, and this is one of the wonderful things I have discovered this summer in working with all these wonderful people, is the music tells everybody something different. And that's what you have to reconcile with the producer of the production. For me, no, I don't have a problem with some of the more modern images in his production because I find them within a nineteenth century framework, which is the framework in which Wagner was working. So I don't have these troubles.

David Littlejohn: You were going to leap in, Maestro?

Donald Runnicles: Yes. I think what one has to remember is, relating back to your original question about what did the actual Maestro want, I mean what did Wagner intend. I think one has to bear in mind two things: under what circumstances was the *Ring* written, and why did Wagner pick a myth? Why did he try to encompass basic world philosophies on four evenings? I think much has been written about this and said about this, but of course a myth is timeless. A myth can be applied, basically, to any period of time and it is important, although I quite agree that the imagination of the listener or the viewer should not be, so to speak, raped, in that he or she is hearing one thing and seeing quite another. But I think it's interesting, having had many conversations on this subject with Wolfgang Wagner (Richard Wagner's grandson), that Richard Wagner himself in 1876 was deeply, deeply unhappy with the premiere of the piece, with the production, with everything about it, and it is, in fact, on record that he said he would do the whole thing completely differently under completely different circumstances. Though it's not much of advertisement for Bayreuth, I think Wolfgang Wagner and the grandchildren always had this in the back of their minds, that Wagner himself was the innovator. He himself was breaking every possible rule in 1876 with his *Ring*.

For instance, we tend to forget that it's due to Wagner that the auditorium is dark for a performance. He was the first one who said, look, in order to focus the attention as in a cinema—imagine in the cinema if the lights were on all the time? I think then you would have an idea of what it would be like in a theatre. This was his innovation. Also, it was his own opera house and he made another innovation by having the orchestra invisible. I think that the man himself was very far ahead of his time. However, I'm not for taking the *Ring* and its significance completely out of context. In one production I won't name and perhaps shouldn't remember, when Siegfried arrives in the first act of *Götterdämmering* and asks, "Who's going to take care of my horse?" Hagen says, "I'll take care of it," and Siegfried gives him his car keys.

That is another whole topic, the extent to which the imagination can become a little bit overburdened, particularly in this experimental age. So what I mean by all this is that Wagner himself was the innovator. Wolfgang Wagner always talks about Bayreuth being a workshop. To approach Wagner, not for the sake of difference, but to try and find what is there. As I'm sure we would all agree, there is so much in the *Ring* that every time you dip into it there's something new. The importance of a myth is the fact that it can be related to every age. With a good producer and director and with an imaginative stage designer, I don't think one ought to say no to contemporary productions.

Steven Sokolow: Peter Ostwald told me that I speak for the audience, so I have the numbers on my side.

He didn't have to twist my arm because when I found out whom I was going to be sitting with on the panel, that's a dream for this "member of the audience." And I can't believe that I'm going to start out by disagreeing with these people. I was thrilled by the Harry Kupfer *Ring* in Bayreuth in 1988 which had many of the anachronisms we have spoken about, but I'd like to change the focus a little bit. I started out getting involved in Wagner long before I saw anything on stage. I was listening to Hans Hotter on records and forming my own images, and I buy the idea that the work is timeless. It seems that very often when we talk about productions we're talking about the scenery and the costumes. I focus much more on the characters and the interactions between them. So when something happens as happened between Brünnhilde and Wotan in their scene, and Siegmund and Sieglinde at last night's performance I really don't care how they're dressed, or how the stage looks, but I go to these music dramas to see those characters interact. And that turns out to be crucial for me.

David Littlejohn: We actually have two people here . . . If I'm not mistaken. Mr. Mazura, you were in the Kupfer production, too, were you not?

Franz Mazura: That is correct.

David Littlejohn: And of course Hans Hotter was in the earliest Wieland Wagner production at Bayreuth, and in both of those cases the listening world was shocked. Critics were flabbergasted. Members of Wagnerian societies were outraged. Not all of them. But in both the early 1950s and then again in 1988, you were participating in productions of the *Ring* that outraged a great many people. I take it you were comfortable with the productions? Mr. Mazura?

Franz Mazura: With my part specially, yes. It was absolutely perfect. The character was the same as in a normal production. What was missing for me, you see, was nature.

David Littlejohn: For those of you who don't know, that's the one that's set in sort of a giant autobahn heading on forever, with laser beams shot around the theater. I'm simplifying it.

Franz Mazura: Yes, but especially the second act when there are all these scenes in the woods, in Kupfer's version you only had this destroyed world after an atomic bomb. With so much missing you have to come up with all the mood and you need twice the energy and everything to give it to an audience. But about the scandal—that was not the biggest one. The biggest one was the Chéreau production in 1976. I was involved in all of them. But, you know, it's very hard to say.

David Littlejohn: And in 1951 for the one Hotter was involved in? Those were in two different generations but each time, it seems to me, listeners, viewers, were more than astonished and shocked. It took them several years to get used . . . well, . . . the 1988 one, they haven't quite gotten used to yet. But in 1951, '52, '53 . . . by 1956 the Wagner brothers' versions had spread all over the world. But doing it the first time, you didn't miss the horned helmets and the bearskins and the trees and the mountains?

Hans Hotter: I certainly didn't miss it. I have to confess that originally I didn't want to become a singer but a musician. Which is not always the same. So it took me a number of years of operatic practice until I finally decided, with the half-broken heart of a musician, to stay in the singing business. So the actual reason I did not like opera in the beginning of my career has to be because the style at that time was so superficial. And so stilted and so not natural. That was the whole idea. So anything which was new, like Wieland Wagner's ideas in '51, '52, was appreciated.

But we must not forget that a number of the soloists of that period had already twenty years or more in opera singing, as I had. I started in 1930. So for us it was a terrible change. I didn't miss just the helmets but I missed the possibility to express yourself and have the surrounding of sets. Wieland Wagner made it quite clear, you see, that for him the sets were distracting: "What I want is the projection of an artist which is not hindered by all these sets." We felt like being naked, without the usual things. And it took us a number of years until we found that this was the better way, for the acting, too. Wieland even asked us." Don't make any movements. Try to act with your face only. Words, voice, and your face." And that, of course, was a hard thing. And (to Mazura) I remember being told just the opposite of the things you mentioned. Instead, Wieland would say: "Don't make movements, don't act on the accents of the music." And now I must say, looking at some productions I've seen, it's just the point to try to duplicate, to act on the musical actions. So I wonder what Wieland would do, back in heaven. But, on the other hand, looking back after almost forty years, Wieland is now regarded as the classic producer. As you said, in the beginning it was the old Wagnerians who were horrified, the ones who do not walk about, they stride instead, Wagnerian strides.

David Littlejohn: I'm always being reminded by feminist students at Berkeley that men have a way of talking louder and more often and therefore women get ignored. And it's very important, especially with bass baritones, to make sure that we hear from the Waltrautes and Brünnhildes and Sieglindes. Again, how much does the production narrow your own possibility for expression? Herta Glaz or Janis Martin? Are you able to make more of a role in what you regard as a sympathetic production?

Herta Glaz: As to production, I must say that Wieland Wagner's production to my taste was really the best. The characters were so plastic and they really stood out. You see, without being distracted by all kinds of nonsense on stage they really had to be the characters who carried the dramas. And that's what I appreciated the most. I don't think the audience needs all kinds of nonsense on stage and, as you remarked, we take away the imagination if we put too much on stage and don't leave enough for the audience to participate.

There's one thing I would like to say. When I was very young and studying at the Academy of Music in Vienna, my teacher, Rosa Papier, thought I should take advantage of a master class at the Mozarteum with a famous singer who had worked with Cosima Wagner in Bayreuth. And I think you would laugh today at what she taught. Because her gestures were very big, and not always in accordance with what the characters were saying but just big, big gestures. I must say I learned a great deal about the characters from her but I really gave up any ideas of just making movements which didn't make much sense.

David Littlejohn: Janis Martin, the same question? The idea of how much you are able to create the concept of a character? And how much in fact is determined by the director or producer?

Janis Martin: Well, everyone comes in with, hopefully anyway, with their own conception of how they want to do the role and it's always sort of a question of whether you get along with a stage director or whether he brings something out in you and makes you better than you could have been on your own. Lots of times there are very clashing opinions on what the part should be. But usually I get along with everybody. There are times when you have to put it in your pocket and say, well, I really don't want to do it that way but that's the way it has to be in this production so okay. But you have to have a motivation. They have to give you a reason to do it; otherwise just forget it because meaningless gestures are about the worst thing I can think of on stage. And, as Hans Hotter was saying, acting everything on the accent is just terrible but sometimes you have to do it on an accent. Sometimes it would be terrible if you didn't. There are certain productions that may be distracting for the audience, but if the stage director gives you a reason and a good personal staging for it, I think you can be very convincing and sympathetic or unsympathetic, if that's what your character is supposed to be. I don't really think that's a great problem if you have a mind of your own.

David Littlejohn: I'm reminded of a line in Stephen Fay's book about Peter Hall's production of the *Ring* in 1985. He talks about the Loges he was thinking of casting and how he came up to Hall and said, "Well I've got four different Loges, which one do you want?" And he described the four different ways you could do Loge. Peter Hall said, "Actually I wasn't thinking of any one of those but. . . . '' Then he said to Hall, "I'm sorry, that's it. You have to take one of mine." You seem to be more flexible.

Janis Martin: You can usually combine your own ideas with those of the stage director unless there's a complete clash and then one has to go, usually.

Laurie Feldman: I'd like to say that it also works the other way. A stage director doesn't just tell a singer what to do and then the singer does it. A singer often will give the stage director wonderful ideas to build on and use throughout the production. Even if those ideas are not part of the original conception, you may hear a wonderful idea and it may touch off all kinds of fascinating, creative thoughts. And that becomes part of the production. So, it doesn't just go one way. It's definitely a collaboration.

David Littlejohn: Let me ask a conductor, how do you work towards creating a *Ring* that's your own, rather than that of the people you work with? Critics are always blaming conductors for what comes out, so now I'd like to hear what you think.

Donald Runnicles: That is a very hard question. I think that, first of all, one should primarily want to recreate the score the way Wagner seemed to have intended it, so we're back, once again, to this initial question, how does Wagner intend it? I think that the biggest mistake is to approach Wagner's scores with the irreverence of "I want to do it like this, or I want to do it like that." The hardest thing is just to try to work out honestly and objectively what was *intentional* Wagner. I think one of the most fascinating aspects of Richard Wagner is his endless melody concept. The fact that no members of the audience should ever be aware of whether—now we're getting, perhaps, slightly technical—the conductor is in two, or in four, or in six, or in nothing at all. I'm talking about the beats and the bar. It's technical because it affects the flow of the music and if there are any abrupt changes in tempo in Wagner, you can be pretty sure it's wrong. I don't wish to generalize too much about this, but this has been a fascinating aspect of my work with Peter Schneider, with whom I shared the podium for these San Francisco *Ring* cycles. Two conductors working on the *Ring* and how does the orchestra get by? What happens if one comes in and says he wants black and the next one comes in and says he wants white and each has nothing to do with the other?

This was, for me, a very rewarding relationship which was built up over five or six years. We worked a lot together in Bayreuth and in Mannheim on the *Ring.* I mentioned this because Peter Schneider's concern, as well as mine, is to find the right tempos for the operas. And the right tempos are not arbitrary, not fixed. They have also to do with singers: to what extent can Singer A sing it in this tempo? And also to do with the fact that if you take the score of *Siegfried*, for example, every tempo in that piece has been so logically thought out. Wagner is always writing such things as that a quarter-note in the previous tempo equals a half-note of the next section. That is to say, one really should not notice the actual changes of tempo until they have taken place. I think this is the primary thing: just realizing it, just finding it. Things like balance in the orchestra, that's a very individual thing and different from house to house. The easiest place, relatively speaking, is of course Bayreuth, where the covered pit takes care of almost all the balance problems, whereas in an open pit the conductor can make himself extremely unpopular, not just to the singers, but with the orchestra in that he always has to dampen this sound. One must: the orchestra cannot play the original dynamic as it's written anywhere else but Bayreuth. It's also a well-known fact that towards the end of the second act of *Siegfried* there was a point where Wagner took a little break from the piece and wrote a couple of little *divertissements* called *Tristan* and *Meistersinger*, and then came back.

This space of twelve years had completely revolutionized his style of orchestral writing. He already had Bayreuth in mind. He already had the idea of this covered pit so the dynamics change, the orchestration changes. For instance, owing to the position of the orchestra in Bayreuth, the strings are wonderfully placed in order to be able to be heard.

No matter how loud the brass section plays, one can always hear the strings. In Bayreuth one can play the original dynamics. But in a house like San Francisco, wonderful though the acoustic is, we spent quite a few hours just working out the dynamics, having to speak to the orchestral players and telling them this is not a criticism but for certain things to be heard, one has to readjust the dynamics. I would be out in the auditorium, Peter Schneider would be conducting and vice versa. I would be conducting the dress rehearsal while he was out in the auditorium making notes. But perhaps I'm diverting a little bit from the original question.

David Littlejohn: Yours is a vision we very rarely get unless we can attend all the rehearsals. To return to this venue, now we're meeting at a medical school and people have been hearing about how sick Wagner was and how sick Wagnerians were, and all sorts of bizarre, strange, psychological stresses and strains involved in the *Ring*. Two questions: Is this the hardest thing that a singer or musician has to do? I mean, are there extraordinary, exceptional, almost impossible strains and challenges in singing a role in or conducting, producing the *Ring*? And I suppose the second half of that is: how about from the audience point of view? Is it the hardest possible thing that an operagoer can do? I mean, is this dangerous to your health?

Steven Sokolow: I'll take the easy part. Well, let's be as honest as the psychologists here: we're talking about addictive behavior. The people in the Wagner Society would be probably the extreme, but I don't think there's a more dedicated audience around. I was struck today when people were talking about the amazing fact of Wagner demanding a king and getting one. It also occurs to me it's also amazing he found the audience that he demanded, that people are as dedicated to his works as they are. I know of three people in our group who are going to all four cycles. And one of them is a woman who is in standing room for three of the cycles.

People break their necks to get to Bayreuth, which is not the most comfortable theatre in the world to sit in, and there are plenty of people who absolutely can't afford to do it but are willing to turn their lives over if they get the chance. One of our members has been spending the last thirty years painting pictures all based on the *Ring* or Wagner's other operas. I really am interested in the answer to your question because I know that I myself can't eat the day before attending a Wagner performance. I'm too nervous, and it's a real mystery to me how the people on stage can assume the roles they do and go on to lead normal lives.

Hans Hotter: It's not tiring at all. It depends on the person.

Franz Mazura: No, it's not. Look at Hans. He spent his whole life in Wagner singing and he's in great shape.

Hans Hotter: I think it has to do, in the first place, with a solid singing technique, whether you were lucky enough to have a good teacher who led you the right way. And out of my experience working with, for instance, English-speaking singers who had to learn the German language, I think it's just a question of having the right coaches to give the real exact idea of what the pronunciation is. Not this stupid idea that you have to machine-gun the German language. You can pronounce the German language exactly as you do in Italian. Sometimes it's just the refusal of the conductor to help the singers to be good in their diction. That way they can save voice. By not using the right diction, you tend to overstrain your voice and this of course is tiring. But basically, to sing Wagner has nothing to do with getting tired as long as you use the right vocal technique.

Herta Glaz: I completely agree with you. I think it is much more difficult to sing Verdi—much more strenuous, rather than difficult.

Hans Hotter: Depends on the conductor who trains you. There have been so many great conductors conducting Wagner who have saved the voices of so many singers by doing the right thing. Meaning the right thing for the singers.

Herta Glaz: Conductors are our friends and shouldn't be our enemies.

Janis Martin: I think it's also a myth that Wagner wrecks your voice. Because if you have a voice that is predestined for Wagner, then it is just like balsam for your voice. For me, for instance, I started very young and just now in the last ten years, I've really found the parts that I sing the very best. And I've sung Wagner for twenty years and, as David said at the beginning, the cat's out of the bag and you all know I've been singing for thirty years this year. I started when I was 20, so I'm 50 now. And if I've been singing Wagner for over twenty years and I'm still singing—I'm singing Brünnhilde this year—I think it's proof that Wagner does not wreck your voice if you're predestined to sing that. I find that Mozart would be much more detrimental to my voice because my voice is too big to pare it down to that size. I can sing a Mozart role but I don't like the sound of my voice in it because I want to hear something lighter. I think a lot of people push their voices to sing Wagner when they really should be singing Mozart and maybe the other way around, too, but not as often, unfortunately.

Hans Hotter: May I say one thing more? In my very young days when I did my first Wagner, I had a very, very famous conductor and he said to all his young cast, "Think Wagner, but sing Verdi." I would like to add something else that I was told: try to sing Italian *piano* but speak *forte*.

Donald Runnicles: I think there are two inherent dangers in singing Wagner. One is, of course, at how early an age to sing Wagner and which roles to start with. And I think the biggest danger, let's presume one does have a solid vocal technique—the biggest problem is not Wagner, it's the jets that can get you around the world very quickly in order to sing your next Wagner performance.

It seems to me the singers who sang Wagner twenty or thirty years ago were healthier than today's because if you were in Bayreuth, you were in Bayreuth and stayed there for the entirety. You weren't flying somewhere else in between rehearsals to give a repeat performance of Brünnhilde, or whatever. I think this should not be underestimated. I can only say of my own experience now, which is very modest in comparison to my colleagues at this table, but in Germany there are certain young singers. . . . It's a well-known fact that there are not very many Siegfrieds in this world. And as soon as somebody has the feeling, "I can perhaps be a Siegfried," this is an area where the vultures, the agents, the impresarios are all hovering. They smell blood, swoop down, take this naive tenor—naive only in that he is really not aware of what's about to happen to him—and finally he sings his first Siegfried somewhere. He does wonderfully; rave reviews. Then every other intendant or general manager says, "Ah, there's a new Siegfried; have you heard about him?" Good. So he takes a flight to the next place and perhaps he sings this sort of stuff for five years and then suddenly he's not singing it so well. And as quickly as the vultures swoop, so do they—having eaten him up—disappear and move to their next prey. And I think that this in connection with Wagner is a very large problem.

Janis Martin: Donald, don't forget the world is very fast now. And people have a very hard time saying no. Although it's always been hard to say no. I know I said no to Brünnhilde when I was 30 because I started as a mezzo and at 30 when I changed to soprano, that was the first thing that was offered to me. But you still have to know how to say no at a young age and that's the hard thing, I think. To have an objective, a goal, and to know that's where you want to go, but you want to take it slowly and not get there day after tomorrow. If you want to sing a while that's the way you do it. When I started my career, and I'm sure when Hans started his career, you started at the bottom and went up. And today it seems to be the fashion to start at the top, and not be there for long.

Hans Hotter: Perhaps it's the pace of development that you take as a young artist. And I think it has also to do, unfortunately, with the high number of not-qualified leading personalities in our operatic world. Way back, forty or fifty years ago, you had always the possibility to talk to an opera director, or to talk with older colleagues, for instance. Where are the older colleagues in the opera companies now? I'm speaking of Europe, now. There are no ensembles any more, in the sense of the permanent resident companies, so whom can the young people talk to? Their only destiny is to arrive this afternoon and leave tomorrow. There's no chance for them. Therefore, it's a different way of being brought up in this very, very difficult job. It takes a number of years to get through your apprenticeship into the master phase.

Another thing: when you sing in Bayreuth, it's easier because of the marvelous acoustic situation. But singing in Bayreuth and being successful means you get enormous publicity. So that means you are invited everywhere. But to sing in Bayreuth is much easier because of the acoustics, and so after singing a dramatic part in Bayreuth, you will sing it somewhere else where the conditions are different, and it will be harmful for the voice. We must not forget this. This is a most important point in development of young Wagner singers today.

Donald Runnicles: Should Bayreuth be the goal, or should it ever be the starting point in a role? In other words, should singers try it out in Bayreuth? Should singers give a debut with the role? I don't want to tread on anybody's toes here, but I think probably it would be dangerous because there one is given a totally false sense of security in terms of balance and one sings it wonderfully in Bayreuth, but Bayreuth is one house and there are a hundred other houses out there.

Just to recall an anecdote; it's a sad fact of life. When I was working with Georg Solti in 1983 on the *Ring*, he came to Bayreuth and he wanted to change the sound in the house. In Bayreuth, for those of you who are not acquainted with it, there's this shell that goes over the pit. And there is then something that comes down from the stage, that slopes down. It has a cover over it and this cover is the secret, or one of the secrets, of the acoustic in the house. But Solti wanted this cover removed.

One thing one does *not* encounter in Bayreuth is the overwhelming loudness of the orchestra. It's a remarkable acoustic, but not because it's so strong that it always overwhelms you. This would be the case if you took the shell away. But as soon as you take the cover away, then the acoustic in Bayreuth is like any other opera house in the world. On this occasion, I remember that Wolfgang Wagner stood by very patiently and just said, okay, we'll let you do it. He knew that a number of other colleagues before Maestro Solti had done the same thing and then very hastily had it put back on again. And that is what happened because the secret of Bayreuth was destroyed. I tell this because I think it really is a remarkable acoustic but one which is unique.

Hans Hotter: I remember in 1955, we had a *Meistersinger* production and at the request of the conductor they made a lot of holes in the new cover and put it over the orchestra. They had to remove it after two days because the acoustic was so torn and so different. So they went back to the original cover.

Donald Runnicles: How did you feel? Should a singer see Bayreuth as the ultimate or the initial?

Hans Hotter: It very much would depend on the personality of the singer and his way of being brought up. If he has already a certain experience then it would help him in many ways but he still would have to change his mind and his approach to certain parts because Bayreuth is something different to other productions. There are some quite well-known singers who started their careers in Bayreuth, such as George London, Martha Mödl, and Wolfgang Windgassen, at the very beginning. They were not known before they came to Bayreuth. They really made a hit there. But they had some experience.

Donald Runnicles: Yes, but had they sung a role there? Was George London's first Holländer (*Flying Dutchman*) there?

Hans Hotter: Oh, yes. But on the other hand George London was a very exceptional case of a naturally gifted singer who would, I think, more or less have had this voice by nature.

Herta Glaz: But he also had previous experience.

Hans Hotter: Yes, he had sung Amfortas, I believe.

Herta Glaz: Another difference is that they gave you more rehearsals then. What happens nowadays is that people arrive and they don't even know the other singers, you see. I think this is disastrous. I think one should go back to an ensemble where people work and sing and talk things over and then we would have a result which is really good. But going back for a moment to the orchestra, I went yesterday to the performance here in San Francisco and I was very happy about the balance between stage and orchestra. I think it is not absolutely necessary to cover the orchestra. It is very important that the conductor has enough sympathy for the work itself; I don't even say for the singer, which he should have.

Hans Hotter: I think an intelligent conductor with knowledge would realize that the dynamic signs in the *Ring*, for instance, which was meant to be performed only in Bayreuth, that he would consider that the dynamics do not fit into other houses. And I have spoken to many of the most experienced conductors, like Knappertsbusch, and they say this is one of the most important things: you conduct a *Ring* performance in Bayreuth differently from a *Ring*, for instance, in Vienna.

David Littlejohn: I think I must brave my evil sword against the great spear. It's past 6:00. This has been an extraordinary hour-long septet, the likes of which you're not likely to hear again. I want to thank all the distinguished guests this afternoon. It's been enlightening.

Name Index

181

Subject Index

185